THE NOCTURNAL
NATURALIST

THE NOCTURNAL NATURALIST

KELVIN BOOT

with 32 black-and-white photographs by the author
and 46 line illustrations by Derek Duff

DAVID & CHARLES
Newton Abbot   London   North Pomfret (Vt)

To my parents

British Library Cataloguing in Publication Data

Boot, Kelvin
  The nocturnal naturalist.
  1. Nocturnal animals.—Great Britain
  I. Title
  591.941   QL753

  ISBN 0-7153-8421-X

Phototypeset by Typesetters (Birmingham) Ltd,
Smethwick, West Midlands
and printed in Great Britain
by Redwood Burn Limited, Trowbridge, Wilts
for David and Charles (Publishers) Limited
Brunel House   Newton Abbot   Devon

Published in the United States of America
by David & Charles Inc
North Pomfret   Vermont 05053   USA

CONTENTS

INTRODUCTION

Over the last few years there has been a dramatic upsurge of interest in the study of natural history. Indeed the present could almost be regarded as a repeat of the heyday of natural history of the Victorian era, more and better television coverage, well-produced books and increased leisure time all having made us more aware of our environment and of the problems it faces. Even so, half the day is usually lost to us. We sleep during the hours of darkness, therefore missing out on a world of nature as exciting and varied as that of the daylight hours and, because we do not know the creatures of the dark and the lives they lead, many of them are misunderstood or feared. Owls and bats in particular have a massive folklore associated with them. Much of this is myth — unfortunately of demonic origin — engendering terror rather than appreciation.

My interest in the world of the night stemmed from a combination of curiosity and necessity — I wanted to study wild creatures but had to work for a living during the day. The result was revelation; I was astounded at how much could be seen within a small radius and am now convinced that a thorough understanding of an area can only be gained by studying it at night. It is far more difficult to put into words the feeling I get when I am in the middle of a wood watching badgers or by a pond watching and listening to bats; the sense of being a guest of the animals under observation is unique and the pressures and strains of the day evaporate when there is only darkness and the noises of the animals around me.

Just sitting and waiting is always a good technique when it comes to watching nature in the wild — animals are often curious and after all you are something new. There will, however, come a time when you will want to go and find the animals, and this is no easy task for you will be at more than one disadvantage. For a start you are in their world, a world which they have grown up in and know intimately. Also at night you have the limitation of darkness to cope with, whereas the animals show a variety of adaptations which enable them to find their way about. The nocturnal naturalist must appreciate these adaptations and be constantly aware of how each animal perceives its world. Know your animal and try to become like it; practice will make perfect.

It is likely that the majority of animals were once, like us, primarily diurnal, and have only acquired the nocturnal habit as a result of various pressures. If these pressures can be regarded as weaknesses, they can be exploited to help us understand the animals and see them at our leisure. Space and food are always at a premium and there are only so many niches within a particular habitat, especially when it comes to the larger animals; utilisation of these niches, when the dayshift has finished, makes very good ecological sense. Avoidance of predators is another very powerful stimulus, and has undoubtedly been responsible for many animals taking advantage of the greater security of the night hours. But security was short lived for some, and it did not take long for the predators to follow their prey into the darkness. Many of the carnivorous invertebrates such as spiders, some slugs and centipedes have evolved nocturnality partly to this end, and the same goes for most of the mammals, the best example being the bats which are, except on rare occasions, completely nocturnal. Nature red in tooth and claw is not something restricted to the day, the fight for survival carries on under cover of darkness.

Many invertebrates, in particular, are slow moving and especially vulnerable not only from predators but from the environment itself; the special conditions of darkness can provide the protection they need for survival. Worms are a good example. Along with slugs and some arthropods they are not protected by the waterproof coat possessed by their daytime relatives, the insects for example. Waterproofing works both ways, and those animals which do not have it are just as likely to become dehydrated as waterlogged – exposure to the dryness and heat of the day would spell their end, the rate of water loss being too great for them to sustain. Even some of the larger animals, such as the amphibians, suffer the same problems when away from water. The relatively high humidity of the night allows these animals to move freely, instead of always having to secrete themselves beneath a boulder or a log in their own private world of dampness.

It is sometimes difficult for us to understand the senses possessed by other animals, our own are so dulled. Nocturnal animals obviously find their way around extremely well so they must be able to perceive their environment in a way which we cannot. Many invertebrates rely on an acute sense of touch far more sensitive and informative than our own. The vertebrates have had to develop other senses to cope with the problems of the night, each group having developed in its own way according to the life-style it follows and the pressures put upon it. Bats use echolocation, a sense which is only just beginning to be understood.

Many animals rely quite heavily on their sight, their eyes having become far more sensitive than ours to the low-light levels in which they live. The sensitive part of the eye which registers light – the retina – is found on the inner back surface of the eye, and the more light that falls on it the better will be the resulting image. An obvious improvement is to increase the area of the retina and thus the light-gathering power of the eye. Some small mammals have achieved this by having larger eyes; the relatively enormous bulging eyes possessed by the Woodmouse, for instance, are an indication of nocturnality. Again, the sensitive retina is coated with two types of cells each of which has its own function: the cones are responsible for discerning fine detail and colour, the rods are sensitive to light itself. All nocturnal animals with this type of eye have more rods than cones resulting in an eye which has excellent light-gathering capacity. But all these extra light-gathering cells would be little use if they were not connected to the nerves which convey messages to the brain and here space is the limiting factor. The nocturnal eye overcomes this by gathering a number of rods together and attaching them to a single nerve, thus not only making more rods possible, but increasing the light-gathering power of each nerve.

The large retina necessary for accommodating so many rods does however have its disadvantages, not least of which is the increased size of the pupil and therefore of the lens so that the whole eye becomes disproportionate and ungainly. A way around this is to increase the curvature of the lens, and some nocturnal rodents have done this. But in doing so the eye becomes more of a light sensor than a means of detail perception and begins to take secondary place as the most important sense organ.

A special problem arises with those predators, and animals such as deer, which are not totally nocturnal and need to see during the day as well. The predators need sight for hunting and the deer, as potential prey, need to see their enemies from a long way off. A nocturnally adapted eye will not give detailed vision and during daylight its immense light-gathering capacity would result in blindness. A close look at the eyes of a cat will reveal the answer – at night they appear to shine and during the day the pupils are reduced to a slit. This is because behind the retina is a reflective layer called the *tapetum lucidum* which, in effect, pushes the light back in the direction from whence it came. In doing this the retina is

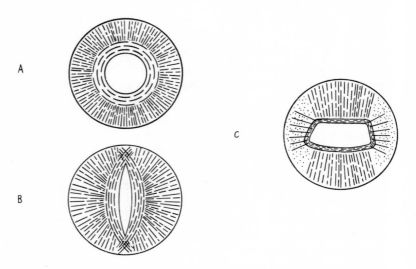

A

B

C

Fig 1   Pupil shapes can betray the lifestyle of particular animals: A typical round pupil of diurnal and strictly nocturnal animals; B vertical slit found in many partially nocturnal hunters; C horizontal pupil characteristic of nocturnal ungulates and other animals needing a wide field of vision to detect predators

stimulated twice. This has the effect of increasing the brightness of the image without sacrificing the ability to discern detail such as happens when an eye has extra rods, though, as with a pure rod eye, there is a high chance of burning out the retina if too much light is admitted. This is where the slit pupil is so important – it reduces the amount of light entering the eye in high light levels. During darkness, on the other hand, it opens up to allow the maximum light in.

The sense of smell is all-important to many nocturnal animals and, watching a Fox hunting or a Badger emerging from its sett, it soon becomes apparent that they are using it to a high degree. A Badger will cautiously sniff the air from all directions to gain a picture of its surroundings and the slightest whiff of danger will send it scurrying back underground. The Fox will be constantly licking its nose to moisten the delicate and sensitive nasal membranes which tell it where and what the prey is.

Hearing is also of great importance. You may think you are walking stealthily through the undergrowth when in reality you will be making a great deal of noise, undetected by the relatively insensitive human ear, but to the keen ears of nocturnal animals sufficient to betray your presence from many yards away. This was brought home to me when I started using a 'bat detector' to track bush-crickets and shrews; it soon became apparent that every careful step I took was accompanied by a cacophony of ultrasound as loud as an army on manoeuvres to the sensitive creatures I was failing to find.

To succeed in any animal observations you almost have to think like the animal itself and be one step ahead all the time. Knowing the senses is a start but you must also know something of the habits of the animal under scrutiny and where it might be at any time. Some owls have a series of perches which are regularly used throughout the night; bats, too, tend to be very regular in their habits emerging at a given time after sunset and following the same route to feeding grounds. Some of the larger mammals follow a regular route around their territory resulting in well-worn trackways. You could do a lot worse than sit quietly up a tree by one of these just to see what comes by. Small mammals have a regular daily rhythm of activity interspersed with periods of rest and there is little point in looking for shrews when they are all asleep. During daylight look for footprints and other signs; try to work out what the animal was, what it was doing there, which direction it came from and where it was going. Look for insect food plants and know what to expect. Animal droppings and carrion are prime targets for nocturnal visitors; get to know where they are and what is likely to visit them. Find animal homes and look for evidence of habitation. Look, listen and sniff. See the world from the nocturnal animals' point of view – the need to find prey without being eaten yourself, the need to find somewhere to hide during the day. Only then will you be allowed into the little known world of the night, a world which takes hold of you and is fascinating and rewarding beyond belief.

The use of Latin or scientific names is essential for a complete understanding of exactly which creature is being discussed. English names are really only of any use in this country and even then there is some room for confusion where local names may differ. The Woodmouse is a good example; it is also very commonly called the Long-tailed Fieldmouse. If the scientific name – *Apodemus sylvaticus* – is used, there is no room for confusion. However, in order that difficult-to-pronounce or unfamiliar Latin names do not impair your enjoyment whilst reading this book, they have been placed together in a separate Appendix (see page 200). If there is any doubt, this Appendix should be referred to. The only exceptions to this are where no English name exists.

1 INSECTIVORES

Shrews

Shrews, like the Mole and the Hedgehog, are members of the order of mammals known as the Insectivora (insect eaters). But unlike Moles which leave obvious signs of their presence or Hedgehogs, which figure frequently in children's story books, the shy retiring shrews are little known. Yet a study of these busy inquisitive animals will greatly repay the time spent on them, if only in pure entertainment value.

There are five distinct species of shrew in the British Isles but only three are found on the mainland and likely to be encountered – the Water Shrew, the Common Shrew and the Pygmy Shrew. All three belong to the group known as the red-toothed shrews. The two species found on the Scilly Isles and Channel Islands are characterised by having no red tips to the teeth and belong to the white-toothed shrews.

All shrews look very similar and are small, pointed nosed, energetic and nervous. Closer examination, however, will reveal differences in size and colour sufficient to tell the species apart, though this is not always easy in the wild and the help of the local cat population in obligingly presenting corpses can be invaluable. Cats rarely eat shrews because of the distasteful substances secreted from glands in the latters' flanks and, when they have finished playing with them, leave the evidence of their night's foraging for all to see. The Water Shrew is the most easily distinguished due to its marked coloration, for unlike the other shrews it is dark slaty-black above and creamy below. The Common and Pygmy Shrews are much more difficult to separate on colour alone, both being light brown on the upper surface and creamy to grey on the underside. The dividing line between the upper and lower surfaces is less distinct in the Pygmy Shrew and a third intermediate colour band between the two is often to be seen in the Common Shrew, but variation in colour within each species causes a great deal of overlap. Colour alone should therefore not be used as identification.

A better guide is size, although even here great caution is needed. As the following table giving approximate measurements for mature animals shows, the Pygmy Shrew is our smallest four-footed mammal – only some of the bats are smaller; the Common Shrew is a little larger, and the Water Shrew is a much larger animal altogether.

	Head and body length		Tail length		Weight	
	mm	(in)	mm	(in)	g	(oz)
Pygmy Shrew	58	(2⅓)	38	(1½)	3.5	(0.12)
Common Shrew	79	(3)	38	(1½)	10.0	(0.35)
Water Shrew	85	(3½)	61	(2½)	13.0	(0.45)

Even in the field, a glance at the relative length of tail should enable you to tell the two *Sorex* species apart – the tail of the Common Shrew is rarely more than half the length of the combined head and body length, that of the Pygmy Shrew is always more than two-thirds.

The food of the three shrews is essentially similar and, despite being classified as insectivores, their prey is by no means restricted to insects. Invertebrates form the main supply for the two *Sorex* species, the Water Shrew in addition regularly takes small fish and frogs. During the winter months, when invertebrate food is scarce, carcases of small mammals may form an important supply of sustenance and also attract any carrion-feeding invertebrates. Under observation in captivity, Common Shrews took eight days and Water Shrews two days to consume carcases of mice.

At first sight shrews would seem to be competing for the

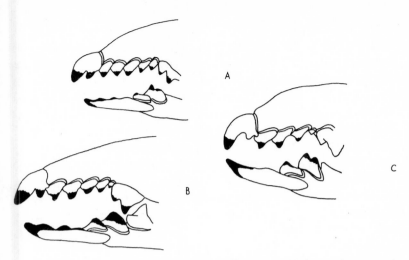

Fig 2   The anterior teeth of shrews are sufficient to tell the species apart: A Pygmy Shrew; B Common Shrew; C Water Shrew

same food and living space but investigation has shown that this is not the case. The Water Shrew, as its name implies, is fond of water and its distribution is closely linked to the occurrence of the clear streams in which it does much of its hunting; indeed in the South East this shrew particularly favours watercress beds. When hunting under water it is greatly aided by fringes of hair on the tail which act like a rudder or keel and on the feet which act as paddles. Excursions into the water are punctuated by frequent returns to dry land to eat the prey caught and to dry out the fur which does not have such efficient waterproofing as that of other aquatic mammals. It is only occasionally encountered well away from water in habitats more normal for the two *Sorex* species.

Both the Common and Pygmy Shrews are found in a variety of habitats wherever good ground cover is plentiful, the Common Shrew usually being the more numerous and often outnumbering the Pygmy Shrew by 8 to 1. On upland areas and sand dunes, however, the Pygmy Shrew is the commoner of the two with the proportion reversed. The rarity of the Common Shrew in these two habitats and the ability of it and the Pygmy Shrew to co-exist in virtually every other situation is a function of their habits and food requirements. The diets of the two have much in common but each has its preferences –

earthworms in the case of the Common Shrew and spiders and harvestmen in the case of the Pygmy. Where the shrews do compete for the same invertebrate group, at certain times of the year, the Pygmy Shrew tends to take the smaller prey (2-6mm) while the Common Shrew relies on larger (4-10mm) individuals. For much of the time the two are also kept apart by vertical distribution, the Common Shrew doing much of its hunting underground in burrows (presumably for earthworms) while the Pygmy Shrew is a surface/leaf-litter hunter. The lack of earthworms and the unsuitable ground for burrowing in wet upland areas and sand, effectively bars the Common Shrew from these habitats.

Woodland, farmland, parks, gardens, wasteland, roadside verges and indeed any patch of land with reasonable vegetation cover should repay a 'shrew hunt', but ditches and hedgebanks are perhaps the most accessible and thus the most convenient places to look. Sound will play an important part in your investigations as shrews are more often heard than seen. The high-pitched screams which accompany a mating fight or a territorial dispute have an obvious function and once heard will always be remembered; the twitterings and squeaks concomitant with shrews' everyday activities are, however, not so easily explained. Some of them are undoubtedly a form of vocal communication between individuals − an indication of presence perhaps, a warning to others of the same sex, or a mating signal to prospective mates. Others seem to be a type of ultrasonic detection system similar to that of bats and useful as a navigational aid amongst the tangle of undergrowth which is the shrew's home.

Chance sightings of shrews running across open areas do happen, but the only sure way of seeing one is to sit patiently, quietly and still, in a suitable habitat. In such circumstances shrews seem oblivious of human presence and will approach very close and may even run over your feet. Although not entirely nocturnal, having at least two periods of activity within twenty-four hours, shrews do tend to have a peak of industry during darkness. For a closer look at them you will have to resort to live trapping (see page 179), which is eminently suitable to the curiosity of these mammals. Shrews,

Page 17 (above) The Common Shrew shows the pointed snout which distinguishes these fussy creatures from all other mammals; *(below)* the Hedgehog is perhaps our most familiar nocturnal mammal and regularly takes a snack of milk and bread in suburban gardens

Page 18 (above) Moles do not like to be above ground but they are often seen at the end of the summer when they are searching for new territories; the spade-like fore feet are used for digging; (*below*) a family of five Badgers is unperturbed by flashlight as they play around the entrance to their sett; the black-and-white head of the Badger can be seen in all but the poorest light

in fact, are often inadvertently trapped in cast-off bottles, drinks cans and crisp packets, all of which are worth investigation, if only for the remains of the victims.

Hedgehogs

The largest of the British insectivores, the Hedgehog is familiar to most people even if they have never seen one and it cannot easily be mistaken for any other indigenous mammal. Confusion can only arise if an encounter is made with one of the Porcupines which from time to time have escaped from captivity and may still be established in plantations near Okehampton in Devon. Even a mature Hedgehog is much smaller, (being only about a quarter the size of a Porcupine) attaining a body length of around 200mm (8in) and a weight of up to 1,200g (2½lb), depending on sex and time of year. Males are usually larger than females and reach their maximum weight prior to hibernation in the autumn. The spines of the Hedgehog and the quills of the Porcupine are both used for defence, but the Hedgehog's are also useful for combing out nesting material and as shock absorbers to break falls. They are generally about 20mm (¾in) in length; the quills of the Porcupine may reach many centimetres.

The Hedgehog is a relatively slow-moving mammal in comparison with others of the same size; so its prickly coat is a particularly useful means of protection. At the first sign of danger, powerful muscles forming a ring around the body contract and pull the Hedgehog's spines erect, while at the same time causing the body to roll into a ball. In this typical defensive posture, it is impenetrable to most predators; only Badgers and some Foxes and dogs are said to have the secret of making it unroll and expose its soft underparts. When foraging, the spines are held flat against the body and so do not interfere with the animal's progress through the undergrowth.

Although the Hedgehog has large prominent eyes, its sense of sight is not good and is probably only used as a last-minute aid to food finding or recognition. Its more acute senses of smell and hearing are employed for long-distance sensing and for gaining information about its environment. The sensitive nose is positioned at the end of the long tapering snout and as such is in the ideal position for foraging in the leaf litter. Most mammals have a wet nose if they rely heavily on the sense of smell; the Hedgehog is no exception and as it approaches its food the sensitive olfactory membrane is liberally supplied with moisture to the point of dripping with anticipation. Food finding is probably only one use to which the nose is put. Just as important is the need to know the proximity of other Hedgehogs and whether these are other males and potential rivals or of the opposite sex and potential mates. A Hedgehog's sense of smell may well be sophisticated enough to impart this information, and may even indicate the age of the newcomer. Individuals may also be recognised by the noises they make. The Hedgehog has a wide repertoire of sounds which we do not fully understand, the commonest being the grunts and snuffles which accompany food searching. Other sounds include a sort of soft chucking sound and, on occasion, an eerie piercing scream associated with distress; very young Hedgehogs emit a kind of whistle.

The Hedgehog is a very successful mammal able to find food and shelter in a variety of situations. In common with other insectivores, it is not restricted to insects as a food source, although they are the most important items for some individuals. Many invertebrates are taken including agricultural and horticultural pests such as beetles and their larvae, slugs, snails and millipedes. Small vertebrates are also eaten, in fact it has been stated that the Hedgehog will eat anything it can overpower – frogs, mice, rats, young Rabbits and the eggs and young of birds all appear on its bill of fare. Among the more unusual food items are snakes which, if they are venomous, are provoked into striking the Hedgehog's spines until they are senseless and easy prey. The Hedgehog is not averse to eating dead animals; carrion of all sorts is readily taken and has been used as bait to attract them. This carrion-eating habit has undoubtedly led to the Hedgehog being persecuted as a predator of poultry and eggs; there is no doubt that it will eat the eggs of Pheasant or Partridge if it happens to come across them, but this does not occur often and the animal certainly does not go out of its way to find these nests.

A recently published distribution map for the Hedgehog shows it to be a very widespread animal. There are many gaps in areas where it would be expected but this probably reflects a lack of recorders rather than an absence of the animal itself. High moorland areas and other wet habitats seem to be avoided, but more work is necessary before this can be accepted as fact; a possible reason might be the lack of dry nesting sites. Confirming the absence or presence of Hedgehogs in all areas would be a simple and valuable task which any amateur naturalist could take part in. As a general rule, though, anywhere which provides food in combination with good cover suitable for nesting should harbour Hedgehogs; copses and hedgerows are favourite places but grassy heaths, open woodland and cultivated land are also suitable and parks, playing fields and large gardens have enabled it to spread into the centres of even our largest cities. Manmade habitats are not always good news for the Hedgehog however; feeding largely on slugs and other invertebrates it is particularly susceptible to poisons such as slug pellets, though encouraging nature's natural pest controllers is surely a much more rewarding way of dealing with unwanted garden pests. The advent of the motor car has also increased the number of Hedgehog deaths; indeed for most people the only regular sight of one is as a corpse in the middle of the road and it is a sobering thought that most investigations into the distribution of this animal have been based on road casualty counts. There is evidence that Hedgehogs in some parts of the country have 'learned' not to roll up when threatened by a motor car, but there are still plenty of casualties and, since it would be totally impractical to place hedgehog underpasses under roads, an appeal to drive slowly at night is the only course of action. The Hedgehog Preservation Society has, however, persuaded some local authorities to install hedgehog ramps in their cattle grids to allow these animals to escape a danger which has claimed very many lives.

The Hedgehog is one of the most nocturnal British mammals and is normally active between dusk and dawn. Only occasionally does it venture abroad during the hours of daylight, particularly if it is ill or has not built up sufficient food reserves for hibernation. It is unusual among British insectivores in that it hibernates but, as with many mammals, its sleep may not last the whole winter. Hibernation begins as late as December, the stimulus seemingly not directly connected with temperature but more with the amount of brown fat that has been built up in various parts of the body. Sleep may last until March or April, but one reason for interruption is if the temperature drops sufficiently to be a threat due to inadequate nest preparation. If this happens the Hedgehog then either makes adjustments or moves its nest altogether. The hibernating nest is a much more compact version of the breeding nest, but both are made of vegetation such as dry grasses and leaves which are combed into shape by the animal's spines as it circles within the bundle. Both types of nest are found in similar situations − dry hidden places under tree roots and bramble bushes, and at the bottom of hedgerows. Old burrows of other animals are also used.

The snuffling and snorting sounds which accompany Hedgehogs on their forays are normally the first indication of their presence and, once located, they can be approached very quietly and observed closely with a red-filtered torch. Apart from its usual habitats, mentioned above, roads are a useful place to look, for modern road surfaces tend to hold their heat long after the sun has gone down and are very attractive to the invertebrates which play such an important part in the Hedgehog's diet. Sand dunes are perhaps an unusual habitat, but they are frequented by Hedgehogs and the advantage is that sand holds tracks very well, enabling studies of home ranges to be made with ease. Do not be surprised if your tracking takes you across water and over walls and fences − Hedgehogs swim and climb very well.

Much is still to be learned about the habits of the Hedgehog and only patient watching will reveal its secrets. Luckily, as an animal which has adapted fairly well to living alongside humans, it is a readily accessible subject.

Moles

The Mole is seldom seen, but its cylindrical shape with short but strong spade-like forefeet, pointed snout and dark velvety fur are familiar to all through its role in children's stories. Closely related to the shrews as a member of the insectivora, it can almost be regarded as the end product of evolution to a subterranean existence. While the Common Shrew too spends much time in underground tunnels, it lacks the modifications which the Mole has acquired for its burrowing life-style.

The greater part of the Mole's life is spent in these tunnels which it has excavated for protection and for finding food. Its activity is obvious for the spoil from its labours is pushed to the surface for all to see and for gardeners to grumble about. The number of molehills is no indication of the number of Moles present; 'infestation' is, more often than not, the work of a solitary Mole renewing its own tunnels or perhaps a new Mole taking over the territory of a previous tenant and removing earth in the name of good husbandry. Although there is no hard and fast rule it is likely that, once a tunnel system has been dug and the territory of a solitary Mole established, digging will be reduced to the odd bit of repair work. However, as the tunnels are a source of food – usually earthworms or insect larvae – and act like pitfall traps, the soil

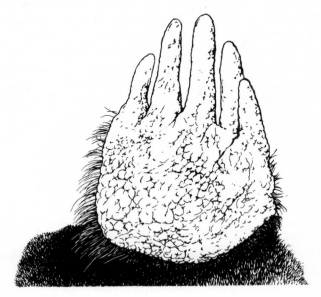

Fig 3   The forefoot of the Mole is broad and strong for digging

type affects the amount of digging. A soil poor in food material means more digging if the Mole is to gain the necessary sustenance for, as is the case with shrews, the Mole needs a constant supply of food to power its bodily functions.

Tagging of Moles with radioactive rings which can be traced underground by Geiger counter has revealed that they have periods of activity lasting about 4½ hours followed by periods of inactivity in the nest of about 3½ hours. Activity is most prevalent during the day, but you are most likely to see a Mole when the light begins to fade at dusk and in the period of half light at dawn. The analysis of owl pellets indicates that Moles are busy on the surface at these times and that they make up a large percentage of owls' prey at certain times of year. On the surface the Mole is at considerable risk from predation due, not as might be expected, to any form of helplessness – the Mole can move at a fair pace for one so ill-adapted to a surface existence – but because of the noise it makes. Moles are not soft-footed by any means, and make considerable rustlings as they move through the leaf litter.

Why then do Moles come to the surface at all? One reason is that, in late summer and into autumn, young but fully weaned Moles are driven out of the parents' tunnel system and disperse to find their own territories and in doing so usually have to move on the surface for at least some of their journey. Many young Moles will inhabit so-called 'superficial' runs under leaf litter or just below the ground surface, if the soil is suitable. These runs are not excavated in the same manner as permanent tunnels as the earth is merely pushed up as the Mole squeezes through the soil. Watching such runs is probably the best opportunity of seeing a Mole as it occasionally breaks surface either by mistake or to survey its surroundings with its sensitive snout, by picking up vibrations rather than by smell. Another more obvious reason for coming to the surface, particularly at night and where there is a well-established tunnel system, is to search for their favourite food – earthworms – as they come to the surface to breed protected by the moist evening air. The third reason why Moles might venture into the insecurity of the open air is to gather nesting material to be taken to the so-called 'mole fortress' – an enlarged molehill, perhaps 300mm (1ft) high and 1m (3ft) in diameter – deliberately constructed as a refuge for resting and rearing young.

The golden rule of the mole watcher is first find your molehills or runs and then wait quietly for signs of activity. Sooner or later you will see the tell-tale vibrations which indicate the presence of an active Mole. Once when I was sitting in the middle of a beautifully prepared football pitch, watching the dawn arrive, a Mole started pushing up the spoils of its labours. Many minutes passed as the molehill got larger and larger, but only once did the pink nose break the surface. Not having the heart to attempt to catch the animal I left it to its work, wondering at the reaction of the groundsman when he found the evidence some time later.

Moles can be found almost anywhere providing the soil is suitable for burrowing and contains enough food. My most unexpected Moles were on Dartmoor at about 457m (1,500ft) in such shallow soil that the surface runs were in places lifting a thin layer of lichen from bare rock. Closer examination revealed deeper soil nearby with sufficient invertebrates for food. Normally, however, the Mole prefers grassland, and originally it was an animal of the woods. Finding Mole evidence in woodland is not easy, especially when the undergrowth is at its summer densest, but patient searching will be rewarded. Even coniferous woodland is worth a close look. At first glance, like moorland, it may not appear to be very productive 'molefood' territory, but you may well be lucky.

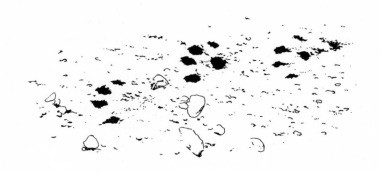

CARNIVORES

Badgers

Badgers have, over the last few years, received a great deal of publicity, so much so that they could arguably be regarded as Britain's best known and most controversial mammal. Badger watching has risen in popularity and has become almost a national pastime; indeed many times when I have discovered a 'new' underground fastness or 'sett' I have also found evidence that it is already under observation. In such cases it is best to look elsewhere and not interfere – one never knows what experiments are taking place and it is so easy to upset results without knowing it. Much of the publicity received by Badgers has come as a direct result of the impassioned debate which followed the gassing programme carried out by the Ministry of Agriculture, Fisheries and Food though the connection between Badgers and bovine tuberculosis is still little understood. There can be little doubt that Badgers do carry the disease, but whether they transmit it to cattle is far from clear, and at the time of writing there is a suspension of gassing while more evidence is collected. I only hope that the protagonists will pool their knowledge for a better understanding of these animals. All too often in the past secrecy and mistrust have put up a smoke screen in front of the real problem; only co-operation will clear the air.

Advances in television technology have done most for the Badger's popularity, and the use of image intensifiers and infra-red filming techniques have brought this normally elusive and nocturnal animal into the homes of millions. It has become a familiar creature and few would fail to recognise it, but familiar though it is most people will never have seen one in the flesh except for an occasional glimpse as it ambles down a dark country lane at night or as it lies as a corpse by the side of the road. Yet the Badger is far more common than these snatched sightings would suggest; it can be found in most parts of this country, is even regularly seen close to human settlements and, in fact, is one of our commoner mammals.

The Badger is the largest member of the order Carnivora in Britain, although until a few centuries ago the larger Wolf and Brown Bear would have taken the title. It is perhaps surprising that, with these two species sadly extinct and many of its smaller close relatives such as the Otter, Pine Marten and Polecat greatly reduced in both numbers and range, the Badger has managed to survive so well despite the efforts of man who has trapped it for food, placed it in barrels, set terriers on it for sport and persecuted it as a supposed predator of game. Even today, although now illegal, badger-baiting and badger-digging still go on in quiet areas of the countryside where people either turn a blind eye or are too afraid to speak out. Some gamekeepers still kill Badgers as game predators, and I have come face to face with a Badger hanging on a gibbet − not a pleasant experience in the middle of the night. But while we shudder and criticise such atrocities we must remember that it is ordinary people who have no grudge against the Badger and wish it no harm who are responsible for many of the deaths, for the single largest cause of Badger mortality today is undoubtedly the motor car.

The other side of the coin is that, since the demise of the larger British carnivores, the Badger has enjoyed a predator-free existence. This coupled with its shy nocturnal habits and the security afforded by its underground setts is probably the reason for its survival, despite the fact that these setts are so obvious and easily found by man. Certainly this obviousness is a great help to the naturalist looking for Badgers and, since it is a reasonably permanent home, watching is made more simple.

The sett itself is characterised by the often massive spoil

heaps which result from tunnel digging. These large mounds seem to flow from the mouth of the sett and occasionally bones are found in this excavated material which is always worth sieving for skulls, teeth etc. Often the earth is mixed with vegetation which is bedding material periodically pushed to the surface for airing; at certain times of year the spoil heaps may consist of nothing else. Warm spring and summer evenings are the best times to see these huge mounds of grass and bracken spill from the sett, and it is during such spring-cleaning operations that Badgers are perhaps easiest to watch as they pass to and fro with old bedding material to be aired or discarded, or with bundles of new material collected from the woods or fields close by. At such times they are virtually oblivious of their surroundings.

The Badger is equipped with a formidable set of teeth which betrays its carnivore ancestry, and it will take many sorts of animal food including voles, shrews, mice, Rabbits and other small mammals. But the most important food item of the Badger is undoubtedly the earthworm, and at certain times of the year when these are abundant it will eat little else. All sorts of vegetable materials are also eaten, especially the underground storage organs of plants such as bulbs, corms and rhizomes. Just what the Badger eats depends on what is available at the time, and thus the diet can vary tremendously throughout the year. It is an animal that takes advantage of changing food supplies — an opportunist, which eats both vegetation and meat, in fact an omnivore.

Watching Badgers is a fascinating and hopefully often to be repeated way of spending the night. But knowledge of the sett and its locality is essential for a successful badger-watch, and so a daylight visit is necessary to decide which is the best place to sit and what are the features around the sett — it is surprising how bushes and branches all turn into Badgers after an hour's wait in the semi-darkness. Although the Badger's eyesight is not particularly sensitive any odd shape in its terrain will be noticed immediately and you should try to conceal yourself as best you can. Sitting with your back to a tree or bush or lying in a hollow should help you blend with the surroundings. Even better is to position yourself actually in a tree if there is a handy one nearby. Badger watching can mean a long wait and you should always ensure that the position you choose is going to be comfortable for the whole night, as on occasion you will have to wait that long; my experience is that cramp always comes at the moment when you least want it. Always test the wind direction and make sure you sit with the wind in your face while facing the sett so that any indication of your presence is carried away. And of course you must keep absolutely quiet as Badgers have very good hearing; if you intend to take photographs at a sett make sure that all your equipment is readily at hand and will not cause any noise as you pick it up.

'Know your Badgers' should be the maxim in your head at all times — which entrances are being used and what direction the Badgers move off in when foraging. The first question is not so easy to answer and experience is the best guide, but there are a few tricks of the trade which can help. Placing crossed sticks over an entrance to a sett in the hope that they will be disturbed by the emerging Badger is an oft tried method which can prove successful. However, as the Badger is an inquisitive animal, the moved sticks may simply be an indication that it has nosed into the burrow from outside. Also the Badger may be sharing parts of its sett with other animals, particularly Rabbits and Foxes. A refinement of this technique is to suspend a strip of sticky tape across the entrance by means of twigs pushed in on either side, the idea being that, as the animal brushes against the tape, it will leave a calling card in the form of a few hairs — a negative result is, however, not

A   B

Fig 4   Crossed sticks across the entrance to a sett (A) will be disturbed by Badgers entering and leaving; hairs will be left on a strip of Sellotape (B)

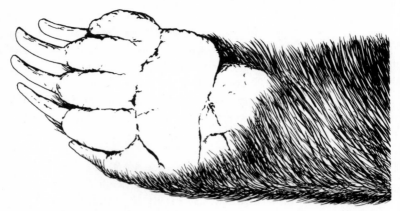

Fig 5 The Badger's foot is superbly adapted for digging – broad and armed with strong claws

always conclusive. In damp conditions footprints leading from within the mouth of the sett can be relied upon, and modern electro-mechanical devices which record the transit of a Badger often give good results. They can be modified quite simply to tell exactly when the animal is emerging, or even for the purposes of automatic photography (see page 192). Deciding the direction of movement of Badgers is simpler, being just a question of looking for the trackways left by the family as it treads its customary way to food, water or dung pits. But avoid these trackways at all costs, as human scent can be quite lingering to the Badger's sensitive nose.

For viewing Badgers the best light is that provided by nature, but often you will have to use an artificial source. Different Badgers react differently to light and, while some will not mind the use of white light, others will be wary even if a red filter is used. The watchword for all nocturnal observation is patience and this is no more so than with the Badger; if at first you don't succeed try again but ask yourself what it was you did wrong. Badgers will emerge all year round and they do not hibernate, but weather conditions can affect the times of emergence. Light levels seem to be the most important determining factor and after dusk is the usual time for the animal to be out and about; though cloud cover can imitate dusk, and at times of heavy cover Badgers are likely to come out earlier than normal. Twilight/nocturnal activity has obvious advantages to an animal that has long been hunted by man who has to rely to a great extent on sight – a sense which is of little help in darkness. During summer months Badgers emerge earlier and are often to be seen before nightfall; such activity being partially due to the shorter night and the consequent need to have sufficient time to collect food, especially if there are cubs in the sett, and partly by the often luxuriant growth of vegetation around the sett which affords greater daylight cover.

The first sight of a Badger as it emerges from the sett is the head resplendent in white stripes as it questions the night air for any sign of an interloper. This is a breathtaking moment and never fails to thrill me no matter how often I see it. After the initial sortie, it may well disappear from view and you will wonder if you have betrayed your presence in some way. Nine times out of ten the Badger will be back after a short while and

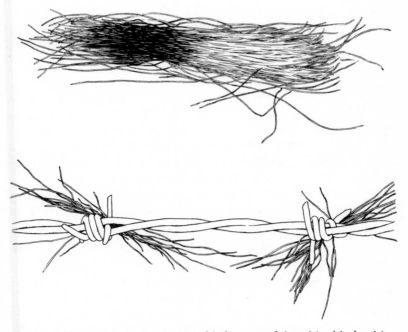

Fig 6   Badger hair is easily recognisable because of the white-black-white striping (above); hairs of many mammals are to be found caught in barbed wire and can give a clue to which routes they use

the watch really begins. Once one Badger has emerged any others normally soon follow, and once on the surface they forage and play with apparent disregard for their surroundings; but do not be fooled — one crack of a twig or the rustle of a leaf will send them bounding back into the sett with a turn of speed unbelievable for such a squat and ambling animal.

The Badger's coloration has puzzled naturalists for many years. Light on top and dark on the underside seems the opposite of normal for mammals; the white stripes on the head, far from being disruptive and thus concealing the animal by a form of camouflage, seem to advertise it rather like waving a flag. Possibly this is of little consequence to this powerful and normally peaceful member of the Weasel family. It is almost as if the Badger is saying, 'I'm a Badger, I have nothing to fear. I don't want to hurt you, but you know I'm here so get out of my way.' Certainly the Badger can be vicious when provoked, and although it will avoid contact with man wherever possible, a cornered Badger is something to avoid at all costs, as many a terrier has found out too late.

Stoats and Weasels

The Stoat and Weasel are the smallest members of the family Mustelidae and being very similar are often confused. Both are long in relation to their width and appear almost snake-like as they weave their way through the hedgerows. In colour there is very little difference; both are reddish-brown on the back and whitish underneath, the Stoat being slightly more yellow than the Weasel. It is also probably the better known of the two species because its winter coat is unfortunately popular as ermine trimming for ceremonial robes. In the British Isles the Weasel rarely assumes such winter garb and thus any white small mustelid seen is likely to be a Stoat. Whiteness has obvious advantage as camouflage in snow and the logical conclusion is that this is its primary purpose; Stoats can however have a white coat when snow is absent and it is more likely that whiteness is a function of low temperatures. In these conditions, a lack of the pigments which would normally fill the hollow hairs results in these spaces being filled with

Fig 7 The Stoat is usually larger than the Weasel and always has a black tail tip

little else but air, thus an insulating cavity is present which helps to keep the animal warm rather like a string vest or double glazing.

Whatever the general colour of the Stoat the tip of the tail always remains black and provides a sure means of telling the two species apart. Size can also be useful as a means of identification. The male Stoat reaches about 300mm (12in) in head and body length and has an additional 100mm (4in) of tail; the female is slightly shorter and averages 200g (7oz), about two-thirds of the weight of the male. The Weasel is much smaller than the Stoat and only just exceeds 200mm (8in) over head and body; its tail is both actually and relatively smaller, appearing almost as if the black tip had been cut off.

Although this size difference is very convenient to the naturalist it is also of immense ecological importance. Both Stoat and Weasel are carnivores and to a great extent share similar habitats; they would therefore be in direct competition for food were they the same size. As it is the food taken is different although there is some overlap. In the case of the Stoat it is mainly birds and Rabbits, in the case of the Weasel it is mainly Field Voles and other small rodents, as well as small Rabbits. Competition for food can exist between members of the same species, as often happens with animals which need a very large food intake to fuel their metabolism. The Weasel, for instance, can have a metabolism up to 100 per cent higher than other mammals of the same weight, this high metabolic rate being a direct result of being long and thin. Animals of this shape have a very high surface area to body weight ratio and are thus very prone to lose heat – a problem not helped by being unable to retain heat by curling into a ball and having short fur which decreases the insulating capacity of the coat. As if this were not enough the Weasel's short legs make food collection less economic, and it is thus restricted to a relatively small hunting area.

It can be seen therefore that at certain times of year when food is at a premium, competition even between the members of a single territory-holding pair could result. It is to overcome this that both Stoats and Weasels have evolved a size difference between the sexes, with the result that the males, being larger, utilise prey too large for the smaller females to overpower. The females, by contrast, are able to pursue smaller prey into burrows too narrow for the males to enter. In effect the two sexes share the available food by concentrating on different facets of it, and the disadvantages of being long and thin are outweighed by increased efficiency of the feeding strategy.

Both Stoats and Weasels are extremely agile and busy animals, constantly on the move and forever looking for something to eat. They remind one of overgrown shrews, investigating everything. Given a suitable habitat in the form of good cover and a plentiful supply of food – lowland or highland, marsh or moor, woodland or hedgerow – neither species should prove difficult to locate. Most often they are encountered quite by chance as they hunt along hedges, below walls or by the side of a woodland ride. The most useful characteristic of both animals is their insatiable curiosity; and just as you want to see them, they will oblige by wanting to study you more closely. Standing still is the best course of

Page 35 (above) A hedgerow sett might at first sight appear to be the result of the use of heavy machinery but careful scrutiny might reveal tell-tale footprints indicating its present use by Badgers

(right) Badgers leave a variety of signs of their presence – a regularly used trackway leading from the sett to the dung pits (in the foreground) is always a good place to await Badgers as they follow their nightly pattern of movement

Page 36 (*above*) A group of Fallow Deer rest after grazing – deer can easily be spotted from quite long distances by the reflection of torchlight from their eyes

(*left*) The Bank Vole as its name implies is to be found along field boundaries and hedgebanks; the blunt nose serves to distinguish voles from other mammals

action once an individual has been spotted; it may disappear into the hedge or a convenient hole, but it will be out again in minutes to get a closer look at you. As both animals hunt along a regular beat, usually at fairly regular times, you will always know where and very likely when to expect a sighting. Locating them by day and returning to the same spot at night is made possible by the fact that both Stoat and Weasel are to some extent diurnal. An absolute giveaway for the nearby presence of a Stoat is the shriek of a Rabbit as it falls victim to the merciless predator. When you arrive at the scene of the kill, the Stoat is still usually hanging onto the victim or dragging it off to a hedgerow lair; if the killer has moved off wait silently and be still, for the Stoat will return for its prize. The Stoat and especially the Weasel can be a serious threat to voles captive in Longworth traps (see page 181), and where these are set the animals should always be expected.

Polecats and Pine Martens

A larger version of the Stoat and Weasel, the Polecat was widespread until the nineteenth century, but is now very restricted in range. Like many predators it has been accused of destroying game and poultry and has thus been persecuted to extinction over most of the country. Wales is now its stronghold and there it has been recorded from every county. In England it is very rare and only found in the counties of Hereford and Worcester, Gloucestershire and Salop bordering Wales, from whence it has spread. As a carnivore, which largely feeds on small mammals, up to the size of the Brown Hare and Hedgehog, birds and numerous invertebrates, its persecution has probably been counter-productive as, had it been given the chance, it would have beneficially destroyed many pest species. Reports of Polecats in areas where they are not well established should always be treated with caution, as many Ferret and Polecat/Ferret crosses are known to have established themselves quite happily in the wild. The true wild Polecat is distinguishable by means of its facial pattern, especially the light band between the ear and the eye, and by its usually darker coat.

Under The Wildlife and Countryside Act of 1981 the Polecat has received some measure of protection and is listed as a Schedule 6 animal, that is it can only be taken or killed by certain methods as stated in the Act. A very close relative of the Polecat and just as rare, the Pine Marten, doesn't receive even this very limited consideration and is still very much at risk in its 'strongholds' of the Scottish Highlands, the Lake District, north Wales and Ireland. Occasionally there are reports from other areas, and those established as accurate seem to be attempts to extend the range either naturally by the animals themselves or as deliberate introduction by man. One recent and very unexpected record from Devon turned out to be the closely related American Marten – an apparent escape from captivity that nobody wanted to admit to owning.

The Pine Marten is a beautiful animal, and although a member of the Weasel family with Weasel-like white underside and shape of head, after a moment's hesitation the difference should become clear. It does, in fact, look very much like a delicate Fox with its bushy tail, chocolate-reddish coat and ears which though not as large as a Fox's are still quite large for a mustelid. Its size is about the same as that of a large cat, and as its footprints can also look very cat-like, no doubt some of the sightings are attributable to felines or small Foxes. Despite its name the Pine Marten prefers deciduous or mixed woodland to stands of pure conifer; extensive planting of conifer plantations over much of its range being possibly responsible, at least in part, for its reduction in numbers.

The much preyed upon Field Vole is the major food of the Pine Marten although it is known to take other rodents, birds, invertebrates and even vegetable food. It is a shame that this animal must be added to the list of carnivores which have been persecuted because of their sharp teeth, and little else.

Mink and Otters

It is strange that many of our native carnivores have been hunted to the point of extinction in many parts of their range, yet an exotic carnivore like the Mink has been allowed to spread almost unchecked to such an extent that experts believe that even the most intensive control programme would now have little effect on its numbers. Originally introduced to this country as a captive mammal for its fur in 1929, since when inevitable escapes have taken place, it is surprising that it was so long before it became established in the wild. The first confirmed breeding populations were discovered on the River Teign in Devon in 1957, and it is now an integrated part of the mammal fauna of many parts of the country with particular concentrations in southern and south-west England, large parts of Scotland, Wales and Lancashire.

The major problem with any introduced species is that it may come into competition with, and if successful cause local extinctions of, the native fauna. Indeed the Mink has been blamed for the decline of the Otter. Studies show however that the Mink and Otter are largely exploiting different food resources. The Mink is catholic in its tastes and can survive quite happily on a variety of foods, small mammals and birds being especially favoured. Fish are also taken, but as far as ousting the Otter is concerned the evidence seems rather to be that where there is a healthy population of Otters, it is they who restrict the numbers of Mink. The decline of the Otter started before the Mink was successfully established in the wild, and so even if there was competition for food it would be hard to prove that this was a direct cause.

Other reasons for the Otter's decline must be sought and there has been a great deal of study to this end. The Otter is at the top of its food chain, having no natural enemies barring humans, and as such would be very susceptible to poisoning of its food stocks. Around the time when the decline of this species was first noticed organic pesticides were starting to be used in large quantities and, while no one would suggest that poisoning of Otters was deliberate and certainly the fishing interests would prevent such a thing from happening, these insidious pesticides would have persisted in the soil eventually reaching the rivers. Invertebrates would have picked them up and fish, by eating large numbers of crustaceans, insect larvae etc, would have concentrated the dosage. By the time the fish were eaten by the Otter the levels of chemical could be quite high, and constantly eating such tainted food would eventually have an effect on the Otter itself. Such poisoning often takes a long time and the animal itself would possibly not die directly, but the reproductive cycle would certainly be affected and the Otters would be unable to produce any young to bolster the population. A similar effect was noticed in some of our birds of prey, where either breeding did not take place at all or, if it did, the eggs would not hatch or would break from being thin shelled. But pollution is probably not the only cause, and the activities of man have had a tremendous affect on this shy and secretive animal – drainage of wetlands, and 'improvement' of river banks for recreation and efficient flow, have reduced its available habitats. Hunting, although no longer a threat, may also have contributed to the decline, especially in a small and vulnerable population already at risk from other factors.

Pesticides are still a problem, despite the introduction of less persistent varieties and much better instructions as to their use, and habitat destruction and disturbance still continue, but the future of the Otter is not all gloom. In 1977 the Vincent Wildlife Trust and the Fauna Preservation Society joined forces to set up the Otter Haven Project which started by finding out as much as possible of the habits and requirements of the Otter and, just as importantly, details of its past and present distribution. Armed with this information they set out to educate landowners and managers of watercourses, with a view to encouraging Otters. The Project does not simply preach, but offers advice and practical help, and a number of 'havens' have been set up along rivers where Otters are known to live or where there is a possibility of recolonisation. It is pleasing to see this work is going from strength to strength, and hopefully it will continue to do so for as many years as it takes to re-establish the delightful, shy Otter as one of the familiar animals of our waterways.

That there is considerable confusion between the Otter and the Mink is borne out by the number of Otter sightings of which I am informed – nearly every one, on investigation, turns out to be Mink. True, in water at a distance they can look very similar, but the larger size and flatter head of the Otter should differentiate the two species; on land the size

difference is even more marked. Few people realise until they
have seen an Otter, just how large it can be – a good 1,200mm
(48in) with an additional 450mm (18in) of tail. The Mink is
much smaller and barely exceeds 600mm (24in) without the
tail. The two species also differ in colour, especially when dry.
The Otter is hardly ever as dark as the chocolate of the Mink,
and lacks the white chin patch which the latter always has.

Finding Mink is relatively simple; watch any stretch of
water in Mink country and one will turn up sooner or later.
Otters are a different proposition; a quiet stretch of a river
well-stocked with fish should be chosen, and if woodland
comes down to the water's edge so much the better as the
Otter requires tangled tree roots for 'holing up' places. (The
temporary resting places are known as 'hovers' and the
breeding sites as 'holts'.) An Otter's territory may stretch up to
5km (3 miles) along such water. Lake and coastal shorelines are
also good places providing there is about 1km² (⅖sq mile) of
water and 2-3km (1¼-2 miles) of shore. Sea-living Otters are
now largely restricted to the wilder parts of western Scotland
and Ireland.

Otters mark their territories by leaving droppings or
'spraints' on rocks, grassy hillocks or low-lying branches at
various places along a stretch of river bank. The same sites are
always used and large boulders along the mid course of a river
or ledges under bridges are very good places to look. The

Fig 8   Otter spraints (droppings) are territorial markers and are left in
prominent positions under bridges, on tree stumps or on boulders in the
middle of rivers

spraints are generally larger than the 'scats' of Mink; but they may be a mere smear or a few fish scales, so much practice is necessary to recognise them. The smell of the droppings can be a good guide to the owner, those of the Otter being pleasanter than the smell of Mink scats. Any animal which uses the same pathways through its territory makes trackways and the Otter is no exception; where there is an obstacle in the river it will take to the bank leaving well-worn paths often with tell-tale footprints.

Foxes

My first sighting of a Fox was purely accidental; I almost tripped over it in the middle of a wood at about 7.30am in broad daylight. The Fox is well known for being at large at early morning in full light and will often lay out during the summer months; my animal seemed totally unconcerned that I was there and simply sloped off into the undergrowth giving me plenty of time to take in the details of his russet coat, pointed erect ears and magnificent white-tipped tail – the 'brush' – all of which are sufficient to distinguish it from any other British mammal. A truly elegant animal, although a member of the dog family it possesses the grace and delicacy normally associated with cats and, like the cat, it is a good climber, although it does need the help of a jumping-off point in order to get itself started on a particularly steep fence or wall.

It is unfortunate that the Fox has been cast in the role of cunning killer, which has led to it becoming a target for huntsman, trapper and marksman, all of whom justify their 'sports' with biased information as to the extent of its ravages and its seeming killing for the sake of killing. It is true that some Foxes become addicted to poultry and cause scenes of carnage both distressing and expensive for the farmers concerned; but tarring all Foxes with the same brush and shooting them on sight is really not a terribly practical way of dealing with the problem. Better security for poultry, in the form of adequate fencing, is much more effective. The Fox is further discredited by its habit of surplus killing and leaving uneaten carcases to further insult the poultry keeper. To us such action does seem wasteful but it has great survival potential for the Fox and in the wild, where food supplies fluctuate greatly throughout the year, surplus killing is reasonably common. Eating less than you kill enables the extra meat to be cached against times of want when other food is not available. Such surplus killing can of course have an effect on the wild mammal or bird life in an area and Foxes must make considerable inroads into the fauna within their territory. Even animals not normally eaten may be caught and cached – the unpleasant-tasting shrews being a good example.

The traditional food of the Fox, prior to the introduction of myxomatosis, was the Rabbit but the consequences of this terrible disease left the Rabbit in short supply and the Fox had to seek another source of food. A ready, if not so large, replacement was the Field Vole; and in some areas, even though Rabbit numbers have increased, it is still the dominant food item in the diet. Many other small mammals are also taken depending on availability, as are small birds at certain times of the year. When vertebrate prey is in short supply, invertebrates are taken including, predominantly, earthworms when these are plentiful. As an opportunist the Fox will rarely turn up its sensitive snout to anything edible and fruits and berries as well as other forms of vegetation are regular supplements to its diet. Scavenging is certainly not beneath its dignity.

Just as the Fox is catholic in its feeding habits, so it is flexible concerning where it lives – any habitat that provides food and shelter will do. Foxes are normally subterranean during the day and the holes (earths) they use can be confused with those of other animals. Both Rabbit burrows and Badger setts can be occupied, even when the original tenants are still in residence. If a Fox is present it is normally given away by the powerful distinctive smell of the earth and the litter of discarded bones at the entrance – the Fox is not very houseproud!

Finding such a hole is a useful start to finding and observing the Fox itself. However, at the earth it is very wary indeed and, unlike the Badger, will not normally stay around long enough to be observed but will rush off as soon as it has emerged. The cubs are a different matter, and will often be seen within a few metres of the hole as they tumble and play while waiting for food from their parents. Adult Foxes are a lot easier to see elsewhere in their territory, and finding feeding grounds or sitting by a regularly used pathway is the best way. As far as their senses are concerned, smell and hearing are keenest and you should always keep the breeze in your face, but their sight is good enough to detect movement and so if a Fox sees you the best thing to do is freeze. Do not attempt to hide yourself or stoop for cover – just freeze. The well-known naturalist, the late H. G. Hurrell, developed a nice technique which allowed him to approach and photograph Foxes very closely; he draped himself in a sheepskin and became a naturalist in sheep's clothing, and very successful it was too.

The scavenging habits of Foxes can be a great help to the would-be observer because it means they can be attracted by a variety of baits; quite accidentally I discovered fishheads to be useful. I had been watching a Badger sett for a few days, the wood was very dark and the Badgers very elusive so that I had heard but not seen them. I decided to use bait and remembered reading that fishheads were irresistible to them. By the time I next got to the wood the fish was very high and oozing unpleasant juices but so as not to cause unnecessary noise near the sett I unwrapped the fishheads some way off, carried the evil-smelling load for a few hundred yards, placed the bait and waited. After about half an hour, just as light began to fade, I heard the tell-tale noises of movement through the undergrowth, but from the wrong direction; the sound was behind me and moving closer. Moving only my head, I caught sight of a Fox tracing the fish drippings to where I was sitting. The wind was blowing across my face and parallel to the sett so that the Fox came closer and closer until it was level with me before it caught my scent. Then, although it was only a couple of metres from me and the bait, its instincts overcame it and it trotted off.

Winter is a good time for Fox watching as they are then less concerned with what is going on around them. This is the season, too, when they betray their presence by their weird screaming mating calls − spine chilling at the best of times but, in the middle of a dark cold wood, an unforgettable experience. Its more normal sound is a high-pitched sharp bark. Both are no longer restricted to the countryside and many a town dweller has been awakened by them in the middle of the night, for the Fox has joined the growing band of animals which are able to live alongside man in his artificial urban environment. Almost any open space is likely to have its resident population so that railway embankments, cemeteries, allotments, derelict gardens, industrial estates and sewage works are fast becoming the ideal place to see Foxes − Foxes which are less timid than their country cousins.

Cats

The inclusion of the Domestic Cat in a book concerned with nocturnal wildlife may seem odd, but as a most efficient predator of small mammals and other animals it is of immense importance. Introduced to this country sometime prior to the Middle Ages as a vermin controller, it has always retained some of its 'wildness', indeed some authorities say that the term 'domestic' is almost a misnomer, particularly in view of the fact that the cat is the only one of our domestic animals which enjoys almost total freedom to come and go where and when it pleases and that during the hours of darkness it becomes a very different animal from the lethargic, affection-ate pet of the daytime.

In many areas of the world where cats have been introduced, sizeable populations have established themselves in the wild state, these so-called 'feral' colonies being to all intents and purposes independent of man although they may scavenge food from his dustbins, live within his buildings or be fed by well-meaning members of the public. In this country 69 per cent of all colonies reported in a recent survey were around hospitals, industrial sites and private residential properties; in the rural setting they centred on farm buildings. The size of a colony seems to be directly proportional to food availability; the largest, with up to fifty cats, were found in residential areas. Around farms the colonies were smaller.

3 HERBIVORES AND RODENTS

Rabbits and Hares

The Rabbit is the most widespread and most commonly seen British mammal. Short-grassed areas are the best places to look, whether manmade, Rabbit made or natural, and playing fields, heaths, moors and open areas in woodlands all have their resident populations. It is almost too familiar to need description, but there are two mammals with which it may be confused – the two British hares. It does however differ in being smaller and in lacking the characteristic black tips to the ears of the latter species. Also when travelling fast the Rabbit tends to hop; whereas the hares, with their long legs, run.

The two British hares are the Brown Hare which is well distributed throughout England and Wales on agricultural land and the Mountain Hare which is a denizen of the grouse moors of western Scotland and the moors of Northern Ireland. There may be occasional overlap of the two species and confusion can arise, especially in those areas where the Mountain Hare has been introduced by man – Yorkshire, Derbyshire and north Wales. Generally the Mountain Hare is smaller than the Brown, has smaller ears and a white tail. During harsh winters, especially in the north of its range, it may assume the white coat, with its camouflage and insulating properties, so typical of sub-arctic and arctic species.

All three – the Brown and Mountain Hares and the Rabbit – have been hunted as pests, for food and for their pelts. But whereas the former have been hunted almost to extinction in some parts of their range and are greatly reduced almost everywhere, the Rabbit shows little sign of reduction in numbers and must rank as one of the most numerous and serious agricultural pests. It is a salutary example of the dangers of introducing any species for, common though it is now, it was probably unknown on these islands until the twelfth century. Originally kept for food and fur, it was largely confined to offshore islands or kept in warrens where its expansion could be checked. But with advances in livestock farming techniques the Rabbit lost its place as the only meat that was readily available all year round, and warrening became uneconomic. Thus warrens were neglected and inevitably many Rabbits escaped to bolster the feral populations which already existed in various parts of the country so that by the 1950s the population had risen to plague proportions and further escalation was only prevented by the introduction of the terrible myxoma virus, which causes the disease myxomatosis. When this virus spread, the Rabbit in this country was all but wiped out. It did not succumb entirely, however, and resistant strains have been building up the numbers once more, although it seems unlikely that the Rabbit will ever be quite so numerous again. Myxomatosis is still with us and outbreaks, indicated by the horribly swollen and weeping eyes, occur from time to time; but changes in the life-style of some Rabbits to a surface-living existence help to

MOUNTAIN HARE BROWN HARE RABBIT

Fig 9   Their size and their black ear tips distinguish hares from the Rabbit. The Mountain Hare also has a black tail base

ensure that the disease has less chance of being transferred from animal to animal by its vector, the Rabbit flea. Within the confines of a burrow system this transference is far more likely.

Most Rabbits, however, still live in burrows; and a series of holes under cover or in a hedgebank are a good indication of their presence, though not necessarily of their numbers. Rabbits do not usually stray more than a few hundred metres from the burrow entrance; they seem to need it close by for a feeling of security and the further they are away from it the more timid they become. On first leaving the burrow they are especially cautious, and any slight disturbance will quickly send them scampering back. Sitting quietly out of sight and smell is the best means of watching the comings and goings at their holes; knowing which animals are higher up the hierarchy is also useful, and can reveal fascinating aspects of Rabbit behaviour. The hierarchy is usually dominated by a female and, as with all colonial dwellers, there is of necessity a strict pecking order and a whole range of complex interactions. A bonus for the watcher is that the Rabbit forms an important food item for other animals, which may therefore be attracted – Stoat, Weasel and Fox should always be expected and are frequently seen. Unfortunately these predators may come upon you before they get to their prey and will then give away your presence; but perhaps next time you can expect the predator from a particular direction and take precautions.

If you need light to help you to see, the faithful red light can be used, but white light is useful too, and many poachers resort to it for rabbit catching because of its weird mesmerising effect. When caught in its beam, Rabbits freeze and allow very close approach before fear of human contact overwhelms the hypnotic quality of the light; which probably explains why many of these animals are killed on our roads, helpless in approaching beams. Many a time I have had to stop my car in order to remove a Rabbit from certain death.

A moving vehicle is an oft used method of poaching Rabbits and one which I have witnessed on many occasions. A couple of times it has brought me close to the same fate. An open space, a still night, myself and the Rabbits in a harmony of observing and being observed, when suddenly there is the sound of an engine, and the brilliant headlights of a Land Rover bristling with hunters and their shotguns. The vehicle screams to a halt, the guns begin, and the rabbits are sitting targets; gunfire is everywhere and the innocent bystander is either not noticed or ignored. Watching nocturnal wildlife can be hazardous!

Hares are not such popular sport these days and most of the marksmen I know tend to respect their rarity and leave them alone. Hare watching is best done at dawn when the hares leave their 'forms', amongst the long grass, to feed and play. They are most active at this time of the day. Although 'mad as a March hare' is a well-known idiom, it's not only during March that crazy hares can be spotted. However, March is the height of the mating season and a marked increase in activity can be associated with showing off and procuring a mate. Watching half a dozen hares bucking, boxing, chasing and leaping whilst you hide quietly behind a convenient hedge is a pleasant way of ending a nocturnal ramble.

Deer

Deer are our largest terrestrial mammals, but are nevertheless elusive and difficult to watch. Being large peace-loving vegetarians, they have been hunted throughout the centuries by predators and latterly by man – a mere glimpse of humans or a whiff of their scent is sufficient to send most deer galloping to a distance or to cover. The technique of studying these magnificent mammals is therefore best learned from an experienced watcher and it is advisable to make contact with such a person at the earliest opportunity.

Deer seem to be well-equipped with all the faculties necessary to avoid being captured, or even observed. Their vision is such that they can see in daylight and also at low light levels – the slit pupil enables them to tolerate bright light, as it reduces the amount of light striking the sensitive retina; at night time, light reflected back through the retina enables them to cope with the darkness. When you hunt deer with a torch the characteristic eyeshine gives away their position but it is a weird experience to come across them in a torch beam.

All you see is a ghostly outline and the pairs of glowing embers in the dark; the heads are always facing in your direction, because the deer will be looking at you before you know of their presence. As with any mammal which haunts the hours between dusk and dawn, the sense of smell is acute. Always approach with the wind in your face. Hearing is also sensitive, and it goes without saying that you should be as quiet as possible – rustle-free clothing is particularly important when it comes to deer.

It may seem from the above that deer watching is an almost impossible task. It is difficult, but success is very rewarding. Basically you have to remain out of sight, out of hearing and out of smell. Climbing a tree in a deer-frequented area is a good method of achieving the required invisibility, but there are not always convenient trees to hand. Sometimes you can provide your own. The 'high seat' (see page 189) is recognised as one of the best ways of secreting yourself from these sensitive creatures and is much used by those involved in deer management – the Forestry Commission for example. Most deer are abroad at dawn and dusk, so you should be in position well before you expect the deer to arrive; the place you choose having been decided by previously looking for signs. For instance, deer are fairly regular in their habits and if woodland species like the Roe Deer are being sought, you will soon

Fig 10   Antler shapes are sufficient to distinguish males of the three species of deer most likely to be seen: (left to right) Red Deer, Fallow Deer, Roe Deer

Fig 11   Fewmets – the droppings of deer – can reveal routeways, numbers and even the physical condition of deer

recognise their pathways through the undergrowth. Patient waiting along these trackways will certainly reap dividends. In areas of damp ground deer leave well-defined footprints – slots. If these are found near a slope, fence or other obstacle which might impede progress, this would be a good place to watch; the deer will be intent on trying to negotiate the obstacle and thus be less aware of your presence. The slots can reveal much to the expert. Sex, age, weight and condition, species and direction of travel are all given away; and if timers are put in the deers' path you will rapidly build up a picture of their movements (see page 198). Droppings, the so-called 'fewmets', can also impart much similar information. When found in large quantities they usually indicate an area where the deer feel comfortable and safe, and therefore a good place to watch. Male deer, especially during the autumn rut, have quite an extensive vocabulary and the species can be recognised by the sound it makes – the roaring of the Red Deer stag is an eerie but familiar sound in its moorland haunts, the Fallow Deer of parkland groans and the common deer of the woodland, the Roe, barks like a dog.

The Red Deer is our largest species and, as its name implies, it is a reddish brown colour. True wild populations exist in

Scotland and north-west England, but there is a thriving population on Exmoor and occasional stragglers wander onto Dartmoor. In other parts of the country the Red Deer has been introduced for decoration and sport and thus may be encountered. Perhaps the most familiar species is the Fallow, which was introduced into this country, possibly by the Normans, although remains in deposits dating back to the Ice Age indicate a previous race. This deer is now a common sight in many of the larger parks throughout the country, and escapes from these semi-domesticated herds have established feral populations in some areas. The antlers of the Fallow stag are distinctively palmate, that is they become flattened towards the tip and have a web-like appearance, and this should prevent confusion with other species. The coat is generally spotted, especially in summer; but colour variations such as the dark form seen in captivity are common. The Roe Deer is a much smaller animal with reddish coat and small branched antlers. It is the common deer of woodlands, but is more often heard than seen, as it disappears into the undergrowth at your approach. The fewmets of this species often go unnoticed on the woodland floor but they are common. They resemble Rabbit droppings but are slightly larger and more cylindrical, pointed at one end and indented at the other.

The Fallow, Roe and Red Deer are the species which are most likely to be encountered but you should always be ready for the unexpected and other species, such as Muntjac, Sika and Chinese Water Deer, have been introduced to this country and are well established in some areas.

Voles

Four species of vole are represented in the British Isles and all show the characteristic vole features of blunt nose, small ears and small eyes, though they vary in coat colour and size. The Common Vole, despite its name, is the rarest species; it holds the distinction of having the strangest distribution of any British mammal, being completely absent from the mainland and occurring only on Guernsey and some of the Orkney Islands. Until recently, the explanation has been that these

Page 53 (*above*) The Snout Moth should be sought on stinging nettles – plants which are attractive to many insects; (*below*) the Lappet Moth is a widespread species found in woodlands, hedgerows and orchards and, like many moths, it is attracted to Sallow

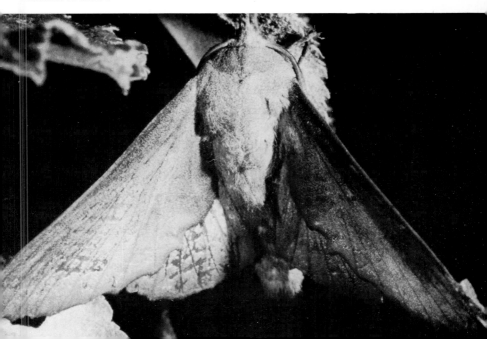

Page 54 The fast-flying hawkmoths are our largest moths; here a pair of Poplar Hawkmoths are mating

voles are relict populations from a previously cosmopolitan species which for some reason was eradicated from the mainland and managed to survive on these offshore islands. Two major considerations arguing against this explanation are that this species seems to manage very well over much of Europe and, secondly, that the various island sub-species seem more closely related to different continental forms than they are to each other. The Guernsey sub-species is very similar to the Common Vole of Germany and is thus probably a relict from when Guernsey was still attached to France but separated from the mainland of Britain. The Orkney sub-species on the other hand shows distinct similarity with voles from southern Europe and is very possibly an import introduced by traders and colonisers about 4,000 years ago. In many respects the Common Vole is indistinguishable from the far more widespread Field Vole; indeed a look at the teeth is the only safe differentiation (see Fig 12).

The Field Vole is probably the most common British species, particularly where there is a good growth of grass, its principal food. Its alternative name is Short-tailed Vole, an allusion to the fact that its tail is relatively shorter than that of the similar Bank Vole, and this is a fairly good method of telling the two apart. Examination of almost any owl pellet should reveal Field Vole remains and a look at the teeth here or in a dead specimen will leave no doubt as to identity. In general its teeth are far more angular and zigzagged than those of the Bank Vole and there is an additional lobe on the upper second molar (Fig 12). The two voles differ slightly in colour, the Bank Vole being more reddish than the usually greyish Field Vole.

Although the Field Vole and Bank Vole live in different habitats there may be some overlap, for instance at the edges of fields where the open habitat of the Field Vole and the hedge-type habitat of the Bank Vole are not easily distinguishable. Both species make quite extensive runs beneath cover, and these should be looked for and checked for droppings as an indication that they are still in use. Fortunately the droppings of the two species are sufficiently different as to be an indication of the species present. Those of the Field Vole are green as

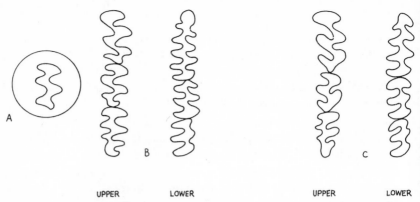

UPPER   LOWER   UPPER   LOWER

Fig 12   A close look at the teeth of voles will help you to identify the species: A Common Vole; B Field Vole; C Bank Vole

a result of its eating grass; those of the Bank Vole on the other hand are browner and tend to be thinner. The runs themselves are also slightly different; those of the Bank Vole being 'tidier' and better prepared. Sheets of corrugated iron and wood are good places to look for both species as they have a habit of building nests under them, and laying down such sheets is a well-tried method of attracting voles for study. Like all the voles, they are delightful creatures and you can observe them quite closely as they go about their business oblivious of your presence so long as you remain quite still – still being the operative word for they have acute hearing and disappear at the slightest sound, which is not surprising as voles have many enemies including most carnivorous species of bird and mammal.

The Water Vole, which attains a length of about 200mm (8in), is much larger than the other three species which are all about 100mm (4in) in head and body length and this always distinguishes it. One of the pleasantest sounds of summer is the gentle 'plop' as one of these animals disappears into a quiet stretch of water as a result of being disturbed while resting or eating on the bank, though by the time you reach the spot all that you see is a stream of bubbles and a dark shape making for the cover of vegetation. Yet although for me at least, this sound is associated with warm summer days, the Water Vole is abroad all year round and, like most British mammals, does not hibernate; in fact during the winter months it is easier to see due to the less dense vegetation. It is also more active at night than during the day so that the best time for observation is the twilight of dusk and dawn.

If Water Voles are in your area they should be relatively simple to find, and any quiet backwater – be it canal, river, pond or drainage ditch – is worth investigation. A 'plop' is a good guide to their presence, and whenever you hear it you should note the location as a possible watching site, the chances being that you have disturbed a vole from a favourite position within its home range of 100m (110yd) or so. Water Voles are burrowing animals and leave evidence of their activities in the form of 'volehills', which look very similar to molehills except that there are usually snipped off grass stalks and other vegetation in the spoil heaps of the Water Vole. Essentially a grazing animal, the Water Vole also leaves signs of its presence along the river bank in the form of closely cropped areas of vegetation, often circular and about 400mm (16in) in diameter, which are especially noticeable near burrow entrances and during the breeding season in spring. The Water Vole is a very noisy eater and I have, on many occasions, listened at the waterside as one munched its way through stems of bankside vegetation only inches from where I was sitting, yet when I parted the reeds to watch, the Vole continued to eat for it was in reality safe in its underground burrow.

Entrances to the burrow system can be at ground level, but are often in the side of the bank either above or below the surface of the water. Where large numbers of Water Voles exist along a canal bank, their diggings can cause damage and consequent leakage and locally they may be minor agricultural pests; but in general these mammals are harmless. Their preference for water, however, makes them very vulnerable to predation from pike, heron, and the Mink and rats which inhabit the waterside, as well as the normal vole enemies.

It is most unfortunate that the Water Vole is often wrongly called the 'Water Rat', a title which has probably subjected it to a great deal of unwarranted persecution. It has none of the undesirable qualities of the Brown Rat with which it is often confused, and is a truly delightful animal to watch. It shows no obvious modifications to its semi-aquatic mode of life, but its typical blunt snout, short ears and small eyes should distinguish it from its less desirable and, at 280m (11in), larger rat cousin.

Observations suggest that small animals are safest during wet conditions as the sound of rain helps to drown the sounds they make as they move through leaf litter as well as washing away their scent trails. The heat loss incurred by having a wet pelt seems to be outweighed by this security, and nights with light rain are, in my experience, the best vole nights. Voles are very curious by nature and readily come to live traps and bait points where they can be watched with the aid of a red-filtered torch. A Water Vole can be tempted to a bait point with an apple or a potato.

Mice and Rats

House Mouse

The House Mouse is renowned for its boldness and has become an all too familiar companion of man wherever he has settled. Although not a parasite in the true sense of the word, it does rely to a very great extent on humans for shelter and food and is a true commensal – a poor man living off a rich man's table – its ability to adapt to a variety of manmade circumstances and foodstuffs ensuring its survival despite the continued efforts of pest officers and cats. Like many of the most widespread animals in Britain, it is not indigenous to the British Isles but is an introduction originating from the steppes of Asiatic Russia. Just when it was first introduced will never be known, but it was certainly before the Roman era.

The House Mouse is easily distinguished from its larger cousins the rats by its much smaller size, having about 80mm (3¼in) head and body length. The tail should be about the same length but is often shortened by close encounters with the local cat population or a mouse-trap. Colour is brownish grey but tonal variation can cause confusion with the much lighter Woodmouse.

Of all the British mammals the House Mouse is the easiest to see, if only because it often comes to you in the comfort of your own home. Quite often a small population of mice manages to exist in relative secrecy, but sooner or later their presence is revealed by droppings, holes in skirting or toothmarks in uneaten food. At first shy and skulking, the House Mouse will restrict itself to those parts of a building where there is little disturbance, but if left alone its fear of man will disappear and it will become very bold. I have watched this species in the comfort of my sitting-room in full light while the television was on, as night after night a couple of mice emerged and followed the same route beside the wall towards the kitchen. In the relative security of a living-room with a sympathetic observer they will even overcome their dislike of being seen in the open and venture into the middle of the room where they can be observed with ease. Eventually my mice had to go; they are after all a source of disease and should be discouraged. Trapping House Mice for study in confinement or for removal to another location is relatively simple because of their following a predetermined route around the house and traps should be placed where the wall meets the floor.

Woodmouse (Long-tailed Fieldmouse)
The best part of sitting in woods at night waiting for a Badger or other animal to appear, is that nature keeps you entertained while you wait and quite often you forget why you were there in the first place – all around are the rustlings, squeakings and other sounds which tell you that you are not alone. Apart from shrews, the mammal which frequently pops up unexpectedly is the Woodmouse.

The Woodmouse is a far more attractive and sleek animal than its similarly sized relative the House Mouse, its coat colour of light russet-brown above and creamy-white below with often a yellow spot on the chest being usually sufficient to distinguish it from that species. Even when there is confusion, especially between young individuals when both have greyish coats, the larger ears and prominent eyes which indicate the Woodmouse's more nocturnal habits provide a ready distinction. It is, in fact, the most nocturnal of all the British rodents, and though it can be seen at most times of the night it has peaks of activity an hour after dusk and again just after midnight.

Just as the House Mouse is often found far from human habitation, so the Woodmouse can be found close to and even within buildings associated with man, especially in rural areas. Essentially, as its name suggests, it is a denizen of woods and other 'wild' places; but it is a widespread species and possibly our most common wild rodent, being found wherever the habitat provides cover and food, including the kitchen garden. As far as food is concerned it is, however, less catholic in its choice than its town relative and is largely restricted to a vegetarian diet of seeds, fruits, buds and seedlings. When these are in short supply, in the earlier part of the year, it may turn to invertebrate food such as insect larvae, snails and even earthworms.

Research has been carried out on the vertical distribution of rodents in their habitats, and the Woodmouse has been found to take advantage of different levels from under the ground to the branches of trees. Whether this is due to territorial competition between other species or even between other Woodmice, or whether it is a result of the need to find extra food is not known for sure. It may be that the Woodmouse is less obvious to predators if it moves silently along smooth branches than it is when travelling noisily through the leaf litter, which is its normal level. Patient observation by an interested naturalist should reveal the reason, but meanwhile this is an area of research open to virtually anyone.

Woodmice are burrow builders and spend most of the day underground, the burrow usually consisting of a ring-shaped tunnel from which other tunnels branch off to a nest chamber and food stores. Obviously, finding a burrow will greatly aid any observations you plan to make and this can be done without too much difficulty. If you are trapping Woodmice, a released individual may lead you to its tunnel entrance – a small hole about 30mm (1in) in diameter. Direct viewing of the mice at night by red-filtered light when, unaware of your presence they collect food from a bait point and take it back to their food stores, will also lead you to their tunnels. Woodmice will readily come to bait points and, after a while, will be almost waiting for you, thus making observation very easy.

Yellow-necked Fieldmouse

Although there should be little confusion between the Woodmouse and the House Mouse, this does not apply to another species, the Yellow-necked Fieldmouse, which may have been overlooked in some areas and thus is possibly more widespread than the records suggest. This mouse is a very close relative of the Woodmouse and is very similar in coloration; indeed only examination in the hand will reveal that it is about half as large again. Its coat is often a richer brown but the most obvious factor, as its name suggests, is the possession of a distinct yellow collar. Even if the yellow spot of the Woodmouse spreads into a line, this is never as complete as the band of the Yellow-necked. Another difference recently detected is in the ultrasonic calls emitted by the two species. The Woodmouse uses a frequency of around 70kHz while the Yellow-necked Fieldmouse seems to be restricted to frequencies of 40 to 50kHz.

Harvest Mouse

The Harvest Mouse is the smallest member of the Muridae, and also the smallest British rodent. At first sight it might be mistaken for the Woodmouse, being similarly russet-brown above and pure white beneath when adult; but its very small hairy ears, blunt nose, prehensile tail and above all its minute size of about 6g (less than 1/4oz) serve to distinguish it from all other mammals. Perhaps the most attractive of its family, its clean-living outdoor lifestyle coupled with its incredible agility in negotiating the swaying stems where it makes its home should endear it to everyone.

Until recently the Harvest Mouse has been regarded as something of a rarity, its scarcity being blamed on the increase in mechanised farming, in particular the use of mechanical reapers and combine harvesters. But surveys over the last few years have established that, although local, where it does occur it is far from rare. The sterling work of Dr Stephen Harris has shown that it is far more widespread than previously believed

Fig 13   Harvest Mouse nests can be found in suitable localities by parting reeds or corn with a long cane; the characteristic ball-shaped nest will be seen above ground level

and that lack of sightings merely reflects its being overlooked by naturalists. Just why it has been missed is a mystery, for this mouse more than any other leaves signs of its presence for all to see. During the summer months it builds and lives in a beautiful intricate nest, globular in shape and constructed from the stripped leaves of grasses, cereal crops, willowherb or other tall vegetation. This nest is usually positioned above ground level, and is thus free from the danger of flooding experienced by ground-living mammals. Such a location also enables the Harvest Mouse to take advantage of the wetter habitats unsuitable for other species and I have found nests suspended in reeds, some 600mm (2ft) above the surface of a pond 300mm (1ft) deep. The mouse's movement through reeds can be very rapid and it has little trouble in escaping from danger, equipped as it is with a sure grip and a 'fifth hand' in the form of its prehensile tail. Thus although cornfields are the traditional home of the Harvest Mouse it is by no means restricted to this habitat and can be found almost anywhere if the tall vegetation necessary for climbing and nest building is present.

The best places to look for nests are around the edges of vegetation patches; using a bamboo cane to part the growth will enable you to see through it better and will prevent damaging crops or trampling the valuable habitat. Once found, an occupied nest should be approached slowly and quietly, for Harvest Mice are very sensitive to vibrations which reach them through the network of stalks around their homes. Establishing that a nest is occupied is a relatively simple matter for, as you approach, the Mouse may well scurry off through the vegetation or drop to the ground, thus betraying its presence. Movement within the nest can usually be detected from the outside, and can be taken as indicating there are young present. If you have missed the evacuation which invariably accompanies your first visit and all is empty on your arrival, the simple technique of passing a stalk through the nest will enable you to determine whether it is occupied when you next visit. The Harvest Mouse will return and, finding the obstruction through its nest, will remove it or bite it in two; in an unoccupied nest the stalk will remain exactly as you placed it.

Brown Rat and Black Rat

Like the House Mouse, the two species of rats found in this country are not indigenous but have been introduced by man. The Black Rat was the first to arrive, probably in the twelfth century, and was already well established by the time its larger relative, the Brown or Common Rat, arrived in the eighteenth. But no matter what colour or species they are, rats are universally despised and regarded with terror – not surprising as the Black Rat was responsible for carrying the Black Death across Europe in the Middle Ages. The Brown Rat is just as unwholesome a character, carrying many diseases transmittable to man.

The Black Rat is distinguished from the Brown Rat by its relatively larger ears and eyes and an all-round slimmer appearance including the tail. In the hand, if you get that close, its fur is silkier and finer to the touch. The Brown Rat attains a head and body length of up to 280mm (11in) and, as its name implies, is lighter in colour than the usual darker brown, almost black, of its cousin, although colour is not a reliable guide.

As far as rat-watching is concerned, I have never seen a Black Rat in the wild, but probably the comments for the House Mouse and the Brown Rat apply equally to this species. Brown Rats can be found in large numbers in barns and riverside warehouses, and sitting quietly with a red-filtered torch is the surest way of seeing these rodents, if your nerve can stand it. Perhaps a more pleasant way is to find a seaside colony and observe the rats by moonlight as the tide starts to come in, when you will see them scurrying among the seaweed looking for food. The Brown Rat is a very suspicious animal with keen hearing and sense of smell; as such it can prove a difficult mammal to watch and an even more difficult one to catch alive or photograph.

I once spent many evenings trying in vain to get a photograph of a Brown Rat, having found a colony which foraged along a road which ran parallel to an estuary. When the tide was high, the rats abandoned the rich estuary pickings and sought dry land, so that driving slowly along the road I often had a dozen rats in view at once. As soon as the car stopped or the window was wound down the rats departed. On my starting the car again they reappeared – cars they did not mind, people they did. I tried everything to get my picture but all attempts failed, and eventually I gave up. Driving down the same stretch of road a few days later I was amazed to see a fried-chicken box apparently walking across the road. I stopped the car, pinched myself, and tried to remember when I had last had a drink. Satisfied that it was not imagination or hallucination I looked again. Sure enough the box was still progressing to the side of the road. Camera in hand I walked towards the box which, on reaching the side of the road, was lifted from inside and out popped a rat. Totally unconcerned it sat on its haunches and proceeded to wash itself; the camera clicked away, I had the picture. A few days later came disappointment; the processing went wrong and all I received back was a roll of blank film. The story of the one that got away, but it really did happen – at least I think it did.

4 INSECTS

Moths

The largest of our moths, with a wingspan of up to 127mm (5in), is the Death's Head Hawkmoth, so called because of the skull-like pattern on the top of the thorax. The adults of this species are rare, because like many others of this family, the Sphingidae, they are migrants to this country and perish soon after arrival and egg laying has taken place. The larva or caterpillar is much more frequently seen, particularly where there is a crop of potato near by. Like all hawkmoth caterpillars the Death's Head has the characteristic horn, which is incapable of stinging as some people think but is possibly used for display or as a scent gland for defence.

Another member of the hawkmoth family is the Elephant Hawkmoth, a name which seems inappropriate for the delicately coloured pink and green adult but which is descriptive of the caterpillar which in places is very common. The first sign of it is likely to be its droppings, which look far too large for an insect, on Rosebay Willowherb or Fuchsia, its favourite food plants. The caterpillar itself is large, about 127mm (5in) long and as thick as a finger, and its texture and colouring are very similar to that of an elephant's trunk, being greyish green and much wrinkled. The characteristic horn can be seen at the rear of the body, but at the front are three pairs of eye-spots which, when the caterpillar pulls in its head and puffs out the surrounding areas, present a frightening spectacle to any predator. They can be induced by prodding the caterpillar gently. Both caterpillar and adult feed at night, the adult being attracted to sweet-smelling blooms, particularly honeysuckle, which it visits in the middle of summer. It is towards the end of the summer that I receive most reports of 'peculiar snakes' and 'giant caterpillars', for this is when the caterpillars are most likely to be seen as they wander about in typical hawkmoth style looking for suitable soil in which to burrow and pupate for the winter, underground and safe from frost and snow.

The silk moths are members of the Saturniidae and usually associated with hot countries such as India, but we do have one representative of this family in Britain — the Emperor Moth which, when a caterpillar, has an apple-green body covered with small warts from which spring black bristles. This is a common caterpillar of heaths and moors, where it can be found among the heathers upon which it feeds. The cocoon made by the caterpillar as its resting and changing place prior to metamorphosis is an indication of its silk-worm relationship for, constructed in the upper leaves of heather and other plants, it is of a glossy silk material. The adult emerges about April or May and cannot be mistaken for any other insect. The large body and large wings with an eye-spot on each are purplish grey with white banding, and in the male there is a rusty wash overall but particularly on the hind wings. Eye-spots are protective as well as decorative, and a function of the partially diurnal habits of this species of which the males often rest on heather and gorse where they are readily discovered by birds. The eye-spots act like targets and the birds, thinking they are real eyes, peck at these and not the soft body — the wings may well get torn but the insect lives on to breed another day. The females are far more nocturnal than the males and are best looked for at night. If you find one you will be in luck, for the females are expert 'assemblers' (see page 173) and will call all the males in the area.

Apart from this sexual call, the great attraction for moths is light. How to take advantage of this for moth-watching purposes is dealt with on page 175, but why are moths so fascinated by lights in the first place? In many instances it seems to be positively suicidal, the moths beating themselves against street lights and windows until they drop. Observations at light traps over many years have revealed that the worst nights for luring moths, other things being equal, are those when the moon is at its brightest; this would imply that moths are then preferentially drawn towards the light of the moon and disregard the otherwise attractive artificial light source. On a dim night, the reverse happens. In effect what seems to happen is that the moths are confused into thinking that the light towards which they are flying is the moon. Simple really, but just what is the attraction of the moon? In order to answer this question we must look at the habits of the moths in question and some basic reasons for genetic exchange.

Moths, in common with any other organism, need to breed with others of the same species but preferably not with individuals of the same population, in order to produce healthy viable offspring which can continue the line — interbreeding always weakens the population and gives rise to hereditary disabilities which put the species at a distinct disadvantage. But many species of moth are dependant on a particular food plant of very restricted area, and therefore cannot move very far. Other moths have flightless females, and these are obviously not able to move far from where they emerge. These two factors on the face of it seem contrary to good genetic exchange and indeed, if left alone, they would be; but this is where the moon comes in — its influence is strong enough to persuade a moth to fly upwards to a given height, probably controlled by sensitivity to pressure changes. Inevitably the moth will travel horizontally as well, so when it does finally come back to earth it will land in a different place from where it started, with different moths of the same species, but hopefully still near its food plant.

But supposing all the moths from one population were to rise into the air at roughly the same time, surely they would all come down together and the change in neighbours would be minimal. Nature of course has everything worked out. Those moths with flightless females leave their own behind and find a new batch with which to mate and it has been found, although there is still much work to be done on this, that in the case of those moths with females capable of flight the males tend to fly higher and thus introduce the necessary differential.

And while on the subject of flight, one of the most peculiar moths, which amazes me everytime I see it, is the Large White Plume Moth. All these moths have their wings divided up into a number of slender plumes, but in this species the usual two pairs of wings are so sub-divided as to appear to be five. This species is very common in gardens and a frequent visitor at night to a lighted window where its long-legged appearance is similar to that of a cranefly. How this bizarre creature manages to keep aloft is a mystery to me, but it does and is always a welcome sight.

But no matter how important calling and strong light may be, only males are 'called' and problems arise if there is competition from a second light source. Something which moths of nearly all types need is food. Some will eat their own brethren when times get hard, others habitually feed on the larvae of other species and some have special adaptations such as one group of 'microlepidoptera' which does not have the extrusible proboscis of the other Lepidoptera but feeds on pollen when adult. However, there is no more natural way of seeing moths in quantity than by sitting near an attractive food source. Many moths are associated with particular plants which form the major food of either the larva or the adult, and as such may be very local in their distribution -- the Bedstraw Hawkmoth or the Oak Eggar for example. If these species are being sought you must find or provide the food in a suitable area. But the more hit and miss approach of merely placing yourself by a well-chosen stretch of hedgerow or clump of shrubs is often the most rewarding, for here there will be plants attractive to a great many species. Sallow, or pussy willow, is a common tree of damp woodlands and has been extensively planted along ditches and river banks. The catkins, its flowers, are unisexual − that is they are borne on different trees − and both are favoured by many moths which, on humid nights in spring and early summer, flock to them in great numbers. The moths themselves provide food for bats and therefore it is no surprise to see these mammals hawking around and sometimes landing on sallow in search of prey.

Among the many moths feeding will be members of the Noctuidae, for this family is the largest in this country. The noctuids themselves can be quite large, with rather stout hairy bodies and they possess a tympanal organ which probably enables them to register the hunting cries of bats (see page 73). The Red Underwing is one of the larger species and is a familiar sight at sallow. As its name implies the hind wings are heavily marked with a beautiful crimson colour, in contrast to the rather dull forewings which resemble the bark upon which they hide during the daytime.

As the year progresses, different moths emerge to feed and lay eggs. Sallow with its early flowering provides much needed food for those moths which have spent the winter in hibernation, but later in the season other vegetation takes its place. Privet is a common hedging plant, often used in suburban gardens, and when the small creamy flowers come into bloom it is well worth looking at for its insect population. A common visitor is the Privet Hawkmoth with its distinctive black and red striped body. The caterpillar of this species, like all hawkmoth larvae, is large and has the horn at the end of the abdomen; but it is the colour that is most noticeable, being a beautiful apple green with diagonal pinky-purple and white stripes. The lovely, sulphur-yellow Swallow-tailed Moth might at first glance be taken for a butterfly as it rests on Privet, but it is a member of a large family of moths – the Geometridae – many of which have a butterfly-like appearance due to their sleekness and the fact that the hind wings are in proportion larger than those of most moths. The caterpillars give the family its name, which means 'ground measurer', because of their habit of gripping with their prolegs and stretching out to find a twig with the legs proper. Having found a foothold, the rear of the body is pulled up to the front and forms a loop, hence the name 'loopers' given to these caterpillars in many districts. When at rest the loopers, which are brownish or greyish in colour, look like a motionless dead part of the shrub on which they are standing as they hold onto a twig with their prolegs and stretch the body out at an angle.

The geometrids are also interesting because in many species the females are flightless and, with their much reduced or vestigial wings, look rather like spiders. The female Winter Moth is one such example, and when seen on tree trunks is often surrounded by a cloud of males which she has 'assembled' by means of her scent. As its name implies, the Winter Moth is found in the colder seasons of the year and is on the wing, or on foot, any time between late autumn and spring. It favours deciduous woodland where the caterpillar feeds on leaves, and can also be a serious pest on fruit trees when it occurs in large numbers.

Nettles are ubiquitous plants which, because of their tenacity and habit of growing in disturbed ground such as gardens, are too often regarded as useless weeds and pulled up and thrown on to the bonfire. The importance of nettles to insects of all kinds is beyond measure and, rather than being destroyed, they should be encouraged and even cultivated specially – a small corner at the bottom of the garden with a controlled clump of nettles can be as colourful as any flowerbed due to the comings and goings of insect visitors at all times of the day and night. Although the nettles themselves are the major attraction for moths, feeding as they do on the flowers and leaves, another visitor which provides an additional source of food adds to the attraction. If you lift nettle leaves and look on the underside, hundreds of small white aphids are often to be seen and these, in common with the aphids so detested by the gardener, produce what to them is a waste product but to the moths is a sweet-tasting solution of sugar – honey dew. Any sweet-smelling substance will, in fact, attract moths and fallen fruit should always be looked at for its attendant insects. When blackberries are fruiting at the end of summer they are a popular food source for moths of all kinds, and give a new purpose to blackberry picking. But you do not have to wait until fruit or leaking sap provides a focus, you can produce your own sugary attractant (see page 177). But while all these plants and sweet solutions are food for moths, the moths themselves have many enemies at all stages of their life histories, and none is so efficient as the sonar-producing bats. Bats can detect, identify and pursue flying insects at considerable distances, and their acrobatic and very rapid flight makes capturing moths a very one-sided contest. Recent

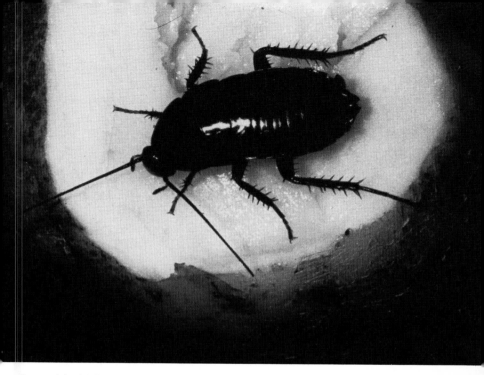

Page 71 (above) The larger cockroaches come from warmer climes; like all others, this Common Cockroach feeds on the rubbish left by humans

(left) Earwigs emerge in large numbers at night – the use of their pincers is still a mystery

Page 72 (above) The long antennae of the largely nocturnal bush-crickets differentiate them from the diurnal grasshopper; the sabre-like ovipositor of this Oak Bush-cricket looks formidable but is not used as a sting – most bush-crickets are harmless although some of the larger ones can give a painful bite; *(below)* closely related to the spiders, the harvestmen are denizens of the night; sensitive elongated legs help them find their way around and locate food

work has shown, however, that the bats do not have it all their own way, and that some moths are able to pick up the ultrasound emissions of some bats even before the bat is aware of the moth. It is then a simple matter for the moth to take the necessary avoiding action.

The most studied group of moths in this connection are those of the family Arctiidae. It has been found that their hearing organ (tympanum) is situated on the thorax just where it meets the abdomen, faces backwards, and consists of a sensitive membrane quite capable of picking up the high-frequency signals of bats. Observation in the wild and laboratory experiments have both shown that these moths, when exposed to such signals, take dramatic action in order to avoid being eaten – loops, spirals and dives are just some of the manoeuvres employed. Photography has helped to explain just how these manoeuvres take place, and shows that in many instances the moth will fly back directly towards the bat and take avoiding action at the last moment, whereupon the bat flies straight past it and misses its meal.

Whilst bats are hunting, their tracking equipment is constantly relaying information about the whereabouts of prey and so it would seem to be in the best interests of a moth to be as quiet as possible. Evidence has shown that this is far from the case, and that many moths transmit their own high-frequency signal back to the bat from another organ on the thorax, thus telling the bat exactly where they are. This would, on the face of things, seem to be a foolhardy way of carrying on, and tantamount to an advertisement. This is exactly what it is; the moth is advertising its presence, but it is also proclaiming something more. The species of moth which are able to emit these sounds are generally those with bright warning coloration which in daylight tells of their poisonous or otherwise distasteful nature. But such warning coloration is not very useful at night when even if the bat's sight were good enough, it would be too dark. The sounds these moths make seem to be performing exactly the same purpose, they tell the bat, 'keep off, I am not very nice to eat', with the result that the bat gives up the chase and the moth lives to see another night. Whether bats have an inherent aversion to such sounds or whether they learn them by trial and error has yet to be established, but the device certainly works.

Beetles

Beetles make good subjects for study for they are virtually everywhere and so not difficult to find; in Britain there are in excess of 4,000 species. Although many can be found in daylight, it is during the hours of darkness that they really come into their own.

Not everyone perhaps appreciates that many beetles are capable of flight – they are furnished, as most insects are, with two pairs of wings. Seen on the ground, they look hard and solid as if they would be very clumsy fliers, and many of them are not very adept at it, but their slow method suits them well enough, and they do not need to fly as often as some insects. The hard outer shell, or elytra, is in reality made up of two reinforced forewings which, when the beetle is not flying, are folded back along the body where they meet in the mid-line. This feature distinguishes them from other superficially similar insect groups, such as the cockroaches whose wing cases overlap and the bugs whose overlapping wings have membranous tips which form a diamond shape. In all three groups the delicate, flying wings are folded up underneath their protective covering.

Often, however, the normal globular beetle shape becomes elongated and the elytra so reduced that, without other distinguishing features, confusion could arise with other insects. The staphylinids or rove beetles could, for instance, be confused with the earwigs, but they lack the latters' 'forceps'. The largest of our many species of rove beetles is the Devil's Coach Horse, a fine insect which should be treated with a great deal of caution as it can deliver a powerful bite, though not a sting as its scorpion-like defence posture might suggest. Most rove beetles are carrion or dung visitors, not to feed on the dung itself but as predators to feed on the other visitors and their larvae. Inspection of these two habitats is looked upon with disbelief and disgust by the uninitiated, but in reality it is a good basic exercise in ecology and, when I read Chapman and Sankey's articles I realised it was a science! They spent some time with their students watching three Rabbit carcases and found that the insect visitors fell into three well-defined groups — those actually feeding on the remains, those parasitising these residents and those feeding on the residents. The first group consisted mainly of fly larvae, the second of various parasitic wasps, and the third, beetles. I have spent many happy hours dung and body watching, but if you are a little shy perhaps you should find a dung heap or carcase off the beaten track — one looks pretty silly sitting, torch in hand in the middle of the night, staring at a pile of rotting flesh or excrement.

Another group of beetles to be expected at carcases are the sexton or burying beetles, so-called because of their habit of burying small carcases below the soil as a food source for their larvae as they first emerge from the eggs laid close by. Most of these are dark in colour but some, like the aptly named *Necrophorus*, are striped with bright orange and readily recognisable. Carabids or ground beetles are also to be found near carrion. They are predators and active hunters as well, feeding on other, live, foods such as slugs and worms.

Beetles are often dismissed as dull and black and, as such, have not received the popularity of the supposedly more colourful groups of insects. But many will, on closer examination, put the butterflies to shame. This is particularly so with some of the very small beetles which have to be studied under a microscope, when they reveal beautiful metallic sheens and a kaleidoscope of colours, iridescent plumes and delicate sculpturing. It is, however, the larger beetles which always attract the most attention, especially when they occur in large numbers for a short period of time. A good example is the Cockchafer, or May Bug as it is called because of its habit of flying for a few weeks in early summer. This large brown beetle, which is often attracted to light, makes its way into dwellings where it is greeted with horror. It is also an unpopular insect with agriculturalists, for its larvae which live underground for three summers do much damage to root crops and seedlings before they emerge as adults. It is a strange quirk of nature that some of man's enemies are also his greatest

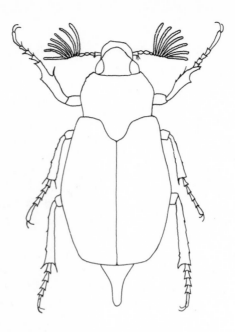

Fig 14 The Cockchafer is an important food item for many animals including the larger bats

allies. Starlings among the birds and bats among the mammals are not exactly top of the list when it comes to most liked animals, yet both unremittingly pursue the Cockchafer as a source of food. The starlings feeds on the larvae, and bats make short work of the flying adults – at certain times of the year the larger bats eat little else. Cockchafers are not as common as they used to be. Insecticides have no doubt done their job well, possibly too well for the bats are also on the decline and it is easy to see a connection – another example of the side effects of man's fight against pests.

Our largest beetle is the Stag Beetle; at about 62.5mm (2½in) it is a formidable creature indeed. Like many other beetles it is found on dead or dying trees, particularly fallen oaks, where the larvae feed on the decaying wood. The Lesser Stag Beetle is found in similar places and seems to be far more common. Both species are so named because of the strange extensions of the jaws which, in the larger species, really do look like a pair of antlers and quite frightening. Strangely, the large jaws of the male are not capable of inflicting a bite whereas the smaller jaws of the female can deliver a nasty nip. The function of the larger male antlers is not fully understood, but is probably to do with sexual display or mating.

Any kind of dead wood is always worth examination; and although when it is dark many of its inhabitants will be on the surface, you should always peel back the bark to reveal the many types of invertebrates which live below it hidden from view. Especially if it is covered with fungi or algae, there will be many different types of beetle grazing on the surface harvest in the cool of the night, the crannies in the bark providing sanctuary during the heat of the day. As with those which live on carcases and dung, these creatures form a tightly knit community, living not just on the wood but also on each other. Oak is a particularly good tree for all sorts of insects and something like 300 species are known to depend on the wood, fruit, flowers, leaves and its other inhabitants for at least part of their life histories. Other trees also support their own communities and they do not always have to be dead – the spread of Dutch Elm disease is a reminder of that. The Elm Bark Beetle, however, cannot really be blamed for the demise of these magnificent trees which have for so long been a characteristic feature of our landscape; it is the fungus they innocently carry which has caused the devastation, though the Elm Bark Beetle inadvertently provides a means of entry as it lays its eggs beneath the bark.

Some of the more beautiful are closely associated with trees, or more correctly with the wood itself. Among these the longhorns must take the prize for their often metallic elytra and, as the name implies, their long delicate antennae. One of the most interesting of this group is the Wasp Beetle, so-called because its yellow stripes with black so resembles a wasp. But the likeness does not stop there; the Wasp Beetle actually moves quickly and taps its antennae in true wasp fashion – a superb example of mimicry. It even moves like a wasp but does not possess the latter's powerful sting; it is charading as something which it is not to gain protection against those animals which are fooled into thinking it can sting.

No account of beetles would be complete without mention

of a true wonder, the Glow-worm. This to me is the acme of nature's attempts at ingenuity, a beetle that can generate its own light — not to see by but as a signal to attract a potential mate from the darkness. Once seen, the pale-green light is never forgotten; even knowing in cold chemical terms the way that it is produced does not lessen ones wonder and disbelief. The steady glow is best seen when the female is transmitting by using the light-emitting patches on the underside of her body, but the larvae, the males and even the eggs are all capable of self-luminescence.

Sadly the hedgerows full of glowing green lights are fast becoming as rare as the stories of elfin lights which they undoubtedly evoked. The reasons for this decline are, as usual, obscure; but it seems likely that ever-present pollution is the key. Increasing use of pesticides is an obvious candidate, but exhaust fumes from cars along country lanes cannot be discounted. Although the adult Glow-worms do not feed much, the larvae are quite particular in their tastes and feed on small slugs and snails. Snails need calcium in order to build their shells so they tend to be restricted to lime-rich areas and these are also the best places to look for Glow-worms.

The chemical process which produces the light involves quite complex changes in a substance called luciferin by an enzyme called luciferase, and oxygen. Often oxidations of this sort produce heat, but in the case of the Glow-worm only light is produced. The luciferin and luciferase are held within the light-producing or photogenic organs to which oxygen is plentifully supplied from the atmosphere via a system of tubes (tracheae) which make up the beetle's breathing apparatus. The photogenic organs can turn off the supply at will, probably by nerve impulses, and therefore the beetle can control its light emissions and turn them on and off at will. Any slight disturbance will cause the insect to 'turn off', and usually this is followed by the beetle dropping to the ground below its chosen vantage point and being lost to the observer. The photogenic organs themselves are of ingenious construction, and ensure that most of the light is transmitted to the outside. The 'skin' or cuticle above them is almost devoid of pigment to the point of transparency, and below the layer which actually produces the light is a third layer made up of urate crystals which acts as a reflector. The whole effect is like that of an electric torch, but without the heat. Again nature was first and more efficient!

Silverfish and Cockroaches

The fact that many animals have found that living close to man provides an easy and comfortable lifestyle is very convenient for the naturalist. Most people do not like sharing their houses with 'nasty' creatures, but on a cold wet night you could do much worse than looking inwards for your studies. Among the commonest insects to be found in the house are the thysanurans, or three-pronged bristle-tails; in Britain there are nine species divided into two families and at least some of these should be found in most dwellings. All of them are fairly small with tapering bodies clothed in shiny scales which rub off when the insects are handled. At the head end are a pair of long, fine antennae, and at the tip of the abdomen are the three long bristles which give the insects their name and distinguish them from other groups.

All the species are nocturnal, shy and retiring. Indeed if it were not for the two members of the family Lepismatidae, which are a familiar sight in households, the group as a whole would remain largely unnoticed by the casual observer. The Silverfish is perhaps the best known of these two species being a common sight in food cupboards where it feeds on spilled sugar, flour and other such substances. The similar looking Firebrat lives in similar situations but, as its name implies, prefers warm places such as bakeries and kitchens. Both species are often seen in daylight, but only when their hiding places are disturbed. They are best seen at night when they move into the open to feed. *Petrobius maritimus* is the largest and most commonly observed species of the family Machilidae. It is abundant on the coast where it is found among stones and organic debris above the tide-line and, like other bristle-tails, is active at night and spends the day hidden away.

Whereas Silverfish often go unnoticed in the pantry, another group of insects make their presence only too obvious by their smell and oily secretions. Although they look superficially like beetles – indeed one species is often referred to as the 'Black Beetle' – the cockroaches are more closely related to the grasshoppers and crickets. Perhaps their most beetle-like characteristic is the possession of a pair of hardened forewings – the elytra – which, as in the beetles, provide a rigid covering to protect the delicate membranous hind wings which may or may not be fully developed and used for flight. But whereas the elytra of beetles meet in the mid-line along the body, the elytra of cockroaches tend to overlap each other. Formerly, cockroaches were included in the same order as crickets because of their many features in common, in particular the long filamentous antennae and the pointed cerci (appendages) at the tip of the abdomen both of which are important sense organs.

The commonest cockroaches are the large species which live alongside man as scavengers and which have led to all cockroaches being viewed with repugnance. The three most familiar – the Common Cockroach, American Cockroach and the German Cockroach are all importees. Originally they lived in warmer climates, but are now spread all over the world wherever man has settled and, thanks to artificial heating, are quite at home in a variety of situations such as kitchens and warehouses. Some live in the heat of decay of refuse tips. Cockroaches are thoroughly nocturnal and only emerge during the hours of darkness to forage for food; at the first sign of light they will scuttle for cracks in floors and walls where they spend the daylight hours. They will eat almost anything, including their comrades – another factor which has led to their success; and given the correct conditions they can reach immense numbers and cause serious damage to stored foods. They must have a keen sense of smell for they are easily attracted to bait traps, beer being a very good lure. The domestic species, because of their economic importance as pests, have been well studied and much has been learned about their life histories. They make ideal subjects for teaching insect structure and as such are much used in schools. Unfortunately the native species have been ignored and little is known of their habits or even their distribution.

There are three species of native cockroach in the British Isles all of which belong to the same genus – the Dusky Cockroach, the Tawny Cockroach and the Lesser Cockroach. The amateur naturalist could very well make a study of these insects, and might provide useful information to fill the appalling gaps in our knowledge. With a maximum length of about 11mm (½in) they are only about one-third the size of the commoner imported species and should not, therefore, be confused with them. Their known distribution is interesting and appears to indicate that they are on the edge of their European range in this country. Temperature seems to be the deciding factor, and they are all restricted to the southern and south-western counties; only the Dusky Cockroach reaches as far north as Leicestershire, and the Tawny and Lesser Cockroaches have been found in south Wales. Although they are essentially ground-living insects, the males of all three species and the females of the Tawny Cockroach can fly. They do this particularly in warm weather, when they become more active and are often found above ground in trees and bushes.

The Lesser Cockroach shows a preference for coastal sites and is frequently found on sand dunes. In general, however, all three species can be found in a variety of habitats including woodland, heathland and grassland. Unlike their foreign cousins, I would not expect to find them indoors.

Crickets

Closely related to the cockroaches, and formerly included with them in the same order (see page 79), are the members of the order Orthoptera – grasshoppers, crickets and groundhoppers. Their general appearance is familiar to most people from seeing the Common Grasshopper, the typically elongated hind legs, modified for jumping, being the most obvious characteristic. Grasshoppers and groundhoppers are distinguished from the other orthopterans by the possession of relatively short antennae – a reflection of their diurnal habits. The largely nocturnal crickets which rely less on sight are furnished with greatly elongated, almost filamentous, antennae.

The Mole-cricket is one of the most bizarre of British

insects; it is certainly one of the rarest and now enjoys total protection from capture, disturbance and destruction under the Wildlife and Countryside Act of 1981. In shape this insect cannot be confused with any other, being about 42mm (1¾in) long and furnished with massively developed fore legs, reminiscent of those of the Mole, and which are used for the same purpose of burrowing into the moist soil of water-meadows and flood plains, its favourite habitat. Warm weather during spring and summer is the ideal time to observe this creature, for then the males emerge to the entrances of their burrows and 'sing' by rubbing their wings together (grasshoppers produce such sounds by the rubbing together of the hind leg and forewing). Although this insect has been recorded from many counties in Britain, it has recently become much rarer and now only occurs in any number along some rivers in Hampshire and Surrey.

Of the ten members of the family Tettigoniidae, the bush-crickets, three are regularly nocturnal in their habits. The Great Green Bush-cricket is the largest member of the order Orthoptera in the British Isles, the females attaining a length of over 54mm (2in); the males, lacking the curved ovipositor, are slightly smaller. Most members of the Orthoptera advertise their presence by means of a song or 'chirping' sound distinctive to each species and the Great Green is no exception; in fact it has the loudest song of all the British species and is best heard during warm weather on summer evenings along the coasts of south and south-west Britain. In the case of the Great Green the song will usually lead you to a clump of reeds, brambles, gorse, nettles or other such shrubby plants. Diligent searching is necessary as the sound produced is somewhat ventriloquial, but patience will result in the exposing of this magnificent bright-green and brown insect.

The Great Green can only be confused with the similarly sized and coloured Wartbiter – a much rarer (and protected), largely diurnal species of bush-cricket – which was indeed once used to bite off warts. The Great Green Bush-cricket can also deliver a powerful bite as I can testify from experience, and should be handled with caution; if you must pick one up do so

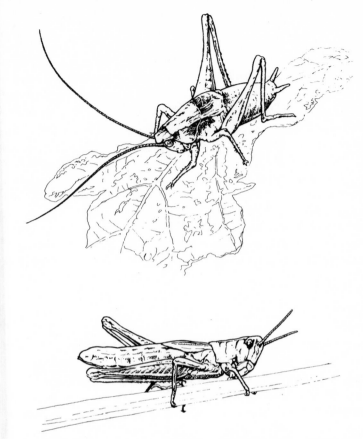

Fig 15 The bush-crickets (above) are easily distinguished from the grasshoppers (below) by their long antennae

by holding it with both hind 'knees' together.

All the bush-crickets crawl or run rather than hop, and when a Dark Bush-cricket scurries across the floor of a house, which it often does, it is regularly mistaken for a spider. This bush-cricket has the same general shape as the Great Green but is smaller and dark brown in colour. It is fairly cosmopolitan in its habitat preferences and as such is probably the most widespread member of its family.

The remaining member of the order Orthoptera which is likely to be encountered during the hours of darkness is the House Cricket which although not a native of this country is sufficiently well established to warrant mention. This insect probably originated in the warmer climates of northern Africa and southern Asia; it is not surprising, therefore, that it should be largely restricted in this country to habitats which provide artificial warmth such as dwellings, warehouses and rubbish tips where the heat of decay provides the necessary temperature. As such the House Cricket is protected from the vagaries of the climate and is therefore not particularly seasonal in its habits, indeed most developmental stages can be found throughout the year. Like all true crickets it possesses long antennae, but is distinguished from the bush-crickets by having a rather globular head. Unlike our other crickets the House Cricket is a good flier and will often take to the wing particularly during warm weather. It is the most nocturnal of all our crickets and its distinctive song will give it away long before it is seen.

Earwigs

Although represented by very few species in this country, and only two of these are anything like common, the earwigs are among the insects most likely to be seen at night when they forage for food. At certain times of year they occur in immense numbers and are an important food source for nocturnal insectivorous predators. Alice Hibbert-Ware in the Little Owl Food Enquiry (see page 117) found that in autumn and winter earwigs were the predominant prey of these owls, and that one pellet examined contained the remains of 343 of the insects. Earwigs actively shun light and the illumination from a torch is sufficient to make them scurry into a hiding place. During the day they remain hidden and are rarely seen unless disturbed. The way they find a suitable hiding place is interesting as they are not completely reliant on the amount of light but, like many dark-loving invertebrates, depend more on the sense of touch. Earwigs are happy only if their bodies are squeezed into a narrow crevice and in contact with the enclosing surfaces − between the petals of flowers, under stones, in cracks in brick walls and tree-bark are all suitable places. Earwigs are also sensitive to moisture and are active in damp conditions, but they always rest in dry surroundings.

There is little danger of not recognising an earwig – its appearance is too well known and, although it is rather like a staphylinid beetle (see page 74), the 'forceps' at the back of its abdomen are absolutely conclusive. These 'forceps' are modified cerci, but they seem ill-formed to serve the sensory function which they perform in other closely related groups of insects. Their shape is somewhat variable and indicates the sex, the males having strongly curved ones while the 'forceps' of the female are almost straight. A so-called 'macrolabious' form in which the 'forceps' are greatly enlarged occurs quite commonly but just why these enlarged forms exist or why there is marked sexual dimorphism has never been explained. It would seem that the 'forceps' play a major part in the breeding process but there is no evidence to support this. There is little doubt, however, that they are used in threat displays, and when presented at the tip of an abdomen curved in scorpion-like fashion they are an imposing sight indeed. This, though, is definitely a case of 'bark being worse than bite', for as weapons of defence they leave much to be desired and can only produce a weak nip at most. If an earwig is threatened it will assume the threatening pose but further disturbance, particularly in the form of vibrations, makes it let go of whatever it is holding on to and simply drop into underlying vegetation and safety.

It has been suggested that earwigs use the 'forceps' as an aid to folding their highly complicated wings and tucking them beneath the greatly reduced elytra – in some species as many as forty folds are necessary to achieve this. However, only one earwig regularly flies – the small species *Labia minor*; the others rarely if ever have need to unfold their wings.

The food of earwigs is varied, but consists mainly of animal matter often in the form of carrion; the supposed habit of crawling into ears and biting through the eardrums is a myth and they are harmless creatures. The alleged damage they do to prize blooms is also a great exaggeration. The earwig is blamed because it remains at the scene of the crime; the damage, however, is most probably caused by another type of creature. Earwigs may take the odd nip at a petal or two, but on balance they are beneficial and to be encouraged in the garden.

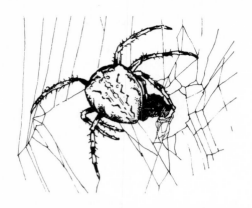

5 OTHER INVERTEBRATES

Spiders

There are about 600 species of spider in the British Isles, and when you consider that there are an estimated 2 million to an acre of grassland it is hardly surprising that these are among the commonest invertebrates encountered by the nocturnal naturalist. To appreciate their numbers you have only to look around on a dew soaked morning as you return from your nocturnal rambles – hedgerow and field alike are strewn with the jewelled gossamer threads of countless spiders. Strangely, in spite of all this beauty they have been little studied, but the more you learn about them, the more fascinating they become.

As a group, the spiders have a colossal impact on the insect life which largely makes up their prey. It has even been suggested that it is because of spider pressure that insects took to the air in the first place. Very early in geological time spiders fed on surface-living prey, their jaws acting like pickaxes to pin their quarry to the substrate. The earliest insects, which did not possess the power of flight, had a very hard time and the ability to fly would have been a distinct advantage. Through various quirks of evolution the insects gained this ability and the relative security of the air. Some spiders, not to be outdone, gave up their largely terrestrial existence and followed the insects, not with flight but by suspending nets – webs – in their flight path. Following the development of the web the spiders themselves had to become modified in order to hunt successfully on these flimsy platforms and their jaws moved sideways to act not like pickaxes but as pincers.

Even among spiders which appear to follow a similar life-style, within a similar habitat there are subtle differences — the orb-web weavers are a good example. Orb webs are perhaps the best known type of web and are epitomised by the typical spider-webs of the large Garden Spider so common in late summer. Any stretch of hedgerow or small area of vegetation tall enough to support this type of web will, on closer observation, reveal a variety of differently sized spiders of the same species as well as a number of different species, all of which build webs at different heights from the ground and at slightly different angles. The structure of the webs also differs from one spider to another — the width of the web itself, the number of radii and the spacing between them are all characteristic of a particular spider and its way of life; the larger stronger webs found nearer the ground are especially good at catching stronger heavier prey such as grasshoppers and crickets. Webs higher from the ground will trap different species of insect, which is not surprising as different insects habitually fly at different heights.

Thus the spiders in any district sort out the available prey amongst themselves and avoid unnecessary competition. Occasionally, however, the wrong prey is trapped and, if it is larger than the web can stand, the spider has to resort to extreme measures to protect its food-gathering equipment. Just as an angler might cut his line to save the rest of his tackle, so the spider attempts to cut out that part of the web containing the offending insect rather than risk destruction of the whole net. The larger orb webs are particularly at risk from accidental destruction by animals and birds; and recent work has shown that the spiders are aware of, and make efforts to counter, this threat. For instance, some spiders build a very special type of structure into the web of a different type of silk from the normal and much more prominent so that it forms a distinct whitish band or segment. This structure is called a stabilimentum for it has always been assumed to be a strengthening device, and it has been shown that small birds make a conscious effort to avoid such webs.

Just like birds during the day, bats at night must present a threat to the security of the web and its spider. Possessed of poor sight and relying much on the ultrasonic sounds they produce to find their way about and secure their food, bats, even if they cannot detect the web, must surely be able to detect a fat spider motionless in the middle of it. And, in fact, many varieties of spider are eaten by bats. But perhaps some spiders at least have a means of defence; it would certainly be advantageous if they could detect a bat's presence long before its arrival. Spiders, in general, detect their prey by means of vibrations and one wonders if they can pick up the ultrasonic pulses of bats in the same way and make a hasty retreat in time to save themselves, if not their webs. There is some circumstantial evidence which makes this seem possible. Firstly spiders possess very sensitive hair-like organs called trichobothria, the function of which is not fully understood but which are known to resonate with certain high-frequency sounds. Secondly there is a precedent for invertebrates picking up emissions of bats in order to protect themselves for, as we have seen, certain moths are able to 'hear' bats and take evasive action. Against this it can be argued that many spiders, particularly ground-living ones, which are out of the catching range of bats, also possess trichobothria; but perhaps this represents defence against shrews which can also use high-frequency sounds and are a major predator of ground-dwelling species. I would be happy if others would follow up my theory and try to reach the answer. My own approach in coming summers will be to ascertain which species of bats, if any, regularly hunt spiders in their webs and just how successful they are. I shall then test the spiders' reaction to ultrasonic sound by playing recordings to them.

Whilst on the subject of sound appreciation, it has been found that different species of spiders react to different pitches of sound, presumably identifying their prey in this way. This differentiation can be demonstrated quite simply by means of a series of tuning forks of different pitch. Each tuning fork is struck and held against the web imitating vibrations which the spider might normally associate with its prey. At the correct pitch the resident spider will rush from its retreat and attempt

Page 89 (above) Centipedes shun light of any sort and only emerge at night to seek their prey; (*below*) two pairs of legs on each segment distinguish the millipedes from their carnivorous centipede cousins

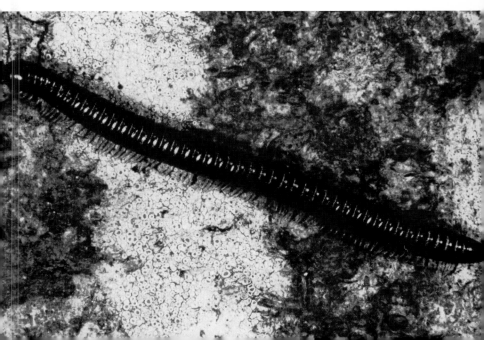

Page 90 (*left*) The humble earthworm provides food for many other creatures including Badgers and Tawny Owls; sensitive to vibration and light they have to be approached carefully and observed with a weak, red-filtered torch; (*below*) sunlight and dryness are the enemies of slugs which emerge at night in large numbers to forage for food

to bite the tuning fork; which also seems to prove that they have little sight discrimination. A common wall-inhabiting spider, which lays a sheet of bluish-white web around its hole, reacts superbly to the key of 'C'. This is a very convenient way of establishing the owner of a particular web, although if other similar webs cross the one you are interested in you may get spiders from all directions.

Not all spiders build orb-type webs and many do not build webs at all, preferring a more mobile existence as active predators. But it is the web builders which are perhaps most in evidence at night when much of the web building and repair work is carried out. The actual construction of webs varies from species to species, but that of the Garden Spider is a readily available example.

First a bridge line is played out on the breeze which carries it to some point of attachment (A). If the spider is satisfied as to the security of this first bridge line she will then walk over it, trailing another line with her. The first line is merely to help her across the gap, the second line is the real bridge and as she proceeds she eats the first. She is thus always suspended between the ends of the first and second lines. Having laid this first foundation line (B), she walks across it back to her starting place carrying with her another line. This line is not so taut and droops below the bridge line (C). At the starting point, the spider attaches this line and then walks back to the middle. Holding on to the middle of the drooping line, she drops off the bridge laying a trail of silk as she goes, until she reaches a point of rest. There are now the first three radii of the web (D). The spider then crawls back to the hub and moves up one of the radii dragging another thread along with her. This is attached about half way up (E). The spider reverses direction and moves back towards the hub securing a line half way down the thread it has just formed. This thread is then carried half way up another radius and attached (F). By continuing this process the basis for the central resting platform is laid down. Moving out from the centre in a spiral the spider first lays down a temporary spiral which is then strengthened and replaced by another permanent spiral which has a layer of gum on its surface and helps to hold any prey which is likely to be

Fig 16   Holding a tuning fork to the web of a spider simulates a captured
fly and causes it to rush out in search of its prey

captured. When first extruded the gum is a layer but as the
spider attaches the spiral to the radii she stretches it or plucks
it causing the gum to break up into a series of beads with non-
stick patches in between.

Orb webs are complicated and many species of spider build
much more simple structures like the scaffold web of the
'Daddy Long-legs' Spider which is responsible for many of the
cobwebs in houses in the southern half of the country. *Scytodes
thoracica* does not build a trap, but takes its net with it and
produces it as need arises. This very pretty southern spider,
striped and spotted, with black on a pale background, is an
active hunter and can perhaps be regarded as a roving gladiator
of the spider world. On encountering prey it casts its 'net'
from a distance and pins its quarry to the ground by two
zigzag threads; it can then approach slowly and deliver the
death bite.

My favourite spider *Segestria florentina* has no accepted
English name. It is a magnificent spider indeed with a body
length of up to 22mm (⅘in) – arguably the largest British
species. Its fearsome appearance is matched by its ability to
deliver a powerful bite which can cause swelling and pain

when delivered in tender skin. A wall-liver, it makes its web
as a series of radii from a central retreat hole, the whole having
the appearance of a cartwheel without the rim. *Segestria's*
elongated body is perfectly fitted to its habitat, its first three
pairs of legs protrude from the hole and touch the radii of the
web, the last pair are directed backwards and anchor the spider
in its retreat. Each radius acts as a trip wire, and any unfortunate creature touching it relays its whereabouts to the
waiting spider which, with a movement so quick as to be
barely discernible, rushes out of the hole and bites its prey –
the latter hardly stands a chance. Even quite large and poten-
tially dangerous insects with stings or bites fall victim, the
prey being pulled back into the hole and its body is folded over
so as to direct any sting or jaws away from its captor. Perhaps
the most spectacular feature of this spider is its 'jaws', the
upper part of which are a brilliant metallic bronzy green, the
overall colour of the spider being a velvety black. *S. senoculata*
is found throughout the country and is about half the size of its
rarer relative *S. florentina*; it also lacks the green jaws and is

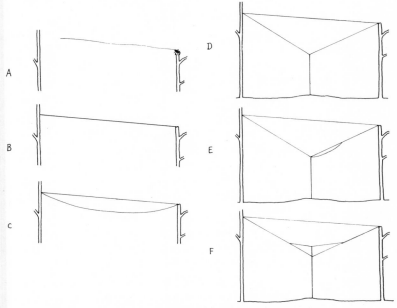

Fig 17   The first stages in the construction of an orb web

much lighter in colour with a distinct pattern of darker lobes down the midline of the abdomen. The two species can thus be differentiated, although care is necessary in the young of *S. florentina* which can look remarkably like *S. senoculata*.

Living in holes in walls would seem to provide the ultimate in protection, but nature being nature there is always a predator at the ready. I have watched both Treecreeper and Nuthatch scouring walls for these species, and one evening one of my prime *S. florentina* fell victim to a playful cat. It has been stated that the best time to see these spiders is on a hot sunny day, and there is no doubt that they are particularly active in sunshine. I have, however, seen more of them at the entrances to their holes in the middle of the night, when their six pale eyes reflect the light from a torch and give them away.

Probably the most familiar and most detested are the House Spiders which, all too often for most people's taste, take up residence in the garage, a cupboard or behind a water pipe, only to emerge at night on the living room carpet, on the ceiling or lie in wait for you as you run your bath. These species, which all look very similar, are the biggest we have; counting leg span they have been known to attain a diameter of 127mm (5in). These spiders are responsible for the sheet webs which seem to adorn every basement and garden shed, collecting fallen plaster and other debris; and although at first sight these webs are nothing like as attractive as the orbs produced by Garden Spiders, they are equally sophisticated.

As if to make up for the unattractive appearance of these sheet webs when they are dirty after a few days of catching falling debris, nature has given a close relative of the house spiders the ability to produce one of the most intricate and beautiful of all webs. For most of the summer *Agelena labyrinthica* lives at ground level among grass, heather or other low vegetation in a sheet web similar to that of the House Spider with a tube disappearing into the undergrowth as a retreat. Towards the end of the summer, in August, the female leaves this web and builds another higher up in the vegetation; this second web is not to capture prey but is a sanctuary for her eggs. The web itself is a large, almost globular, mass of web with many tunnels leading into it – a marvel of architecture.

The whole effect is that of a labyrinth, hence the spider's name.

The study of spiders is indeed daunting to the beginner, many species being small, and many only positively identifiable with a microscope and a great deal of difficulty. It is best to concentrate on the commoner more readily recognisable species first in order to familiarise yourself with the terminology which must inevitably accompany all living things. But unlike some aspects of natural history the study of spiders is one that can be carried out almost anywhere and at any time of year. Spiders are amongst the most successful of all invertebrates and can be found living at the sea's edge and at the top of mountains. One of our species – the aptly named Water Spider – has even managed to exploit the world under water, where it swims after prey and even lays its eggs in a specially constructed diving bell which it keeps supplied with oxygen from the surface. Much is still to be learned from even the most common species, and they are often neglected because they are so plentiful. I know that once the spiders in your house or garden have been examined, you will want to continue your study in the great outdoors.

Harvestmen

Another group of arachnids, the harvestmen, spend the greater part of the day hidden and only emerge in large numbers at night. They are also known as 'Daddy Long-legs', but are not related to the Craneflies which also bear this name. Another, perhaps more apt, name is harvest spider, as they have certain things in common with the spiders, the most obvious being the possession of eight legs, which places them in the class Arachnida. But they differ from the spiders sufficiently to have an Order of their own – the Opiliones.

Harvestmen do not have the apparatus to produce silk for webs, nor do they possess a venomous bite and, unlike spiders which have a two-part body, harvestmen appear to have a one-part globular form. Usually they have long flexible legs, although some have short sturdy ones. Each walking leg has seven segments whose relative lengths are important in identifying the species. The first six are usually sturdy; the seventh, the tarsus, more often than not shows extreme elongation and appears to consist of many pieces, the so-called 'false segments', which provide flexibility. In all British species the second pair of legs are the longest and their function is sensory rather than locomotory. When at rest all the legs are arranged in a radiating pattern and act in such a way as to give the animal early warning of approaching danger. Special organs in the legs seem to be sensitive to flexion in the leg joints, so that when a leg is flexed it tells the animal the direction from which the disturbance, and danger, is coming. Such sensitivity becomes apparent when one tries to gain a closer look at a harvestman. As you disturb the vegetation, the animal invariably runs off in the opposite direction.

Harvestmen can be found in most situations, but are particularly numerous in fairly damp conditions where they can enjoy the moisture upon which they rely for survival; their sensitivity to desiccation being one reason why they remain hidden for much of the day. They also drink a lot and need moist ground in which to lay their eggs. As far as food is concerned they are largely carnivorous and will feed on almost anything of suitable size. Food as large as earthworms may be taken; but snails, spiders, flies, other harvestmen and a host of other invertebrates are more usual. They will readily take carrion and often appear at the bait put down for beetles. It is not uncommon for them to visit a sugaring patch laid for moths and other insects.

Late summer and early autumn are the best times to see them, but some species at least can be found throughout the year and in a variety of habitats.

Centipedes

Centipedes are nocturnal predators which feed on a variety of invertebrates including insects and their larvae, worms, slugs and indeed almost anything they can overpower and kill with their poisonous bite. Although some tropical centipedes can inflict a painful bite on man no British species is dangerous, and as they feed on many garden pests they are to be encouraged. Their lack of a waterproof cuticle as possessed by the insects, their dislike of light and the need for the security of being enclosed between surfaces limit them to habitats of high humidity, low light and an even temperature – beneath stones, under the bark of trees, within leaf litter and other debris, even beneath the soil surface, are suitable places. During summer drought and winter cold, when even these habitats do not provide total protection, they may seek deeper crevices in the soil. The nights of spring and autumn are the only times when conditions are right for centipedes to emerge into the open and are thus the best times for the centipede hunter. A bright light will cause them to seek cover so a red-filtered torch should be used.

The Common Brown Centipede *Lithobius forficatus* (order Lithobiomorpha) is the most widespread and most familiar centipede in the British Isles. It shows the general structure of centipedes very well – a serpentine body divided into fifteen segments each bearing a pair of legs and a head furnished with powerful mandibles and poison-bearing fangs. Another member of the same order, *L. variegatus*, is the only centipede, and indeed one of the few animals, endemic to the British Isles and occuring in no other part of the world.

It is amongst the members of the order Geophilomorpha that the popular name for the whole group – 'centipedes' or 'hundred legs' – becomes apt, for the various species possess between 37 and 101 pairs. The legs are short and unlike the other centipedes, the body is long and thin and the joints between the segments are flexible – a reflection of the lifestyle of the members of this order which is essentially subterranean. Movement through soil is facilitated by the serpentine body shape and ability to flex it through 180 degrees; many geophilomorphids also have the ability to move both backwards and forwards with equal facility, the last pair of legs being modified to act as tactile sensors.

Of particular interest is the ability of at least three species of Geophilomorpha to produce light; indeed one species, *Geophilus carpophagus* is locally known as 'glow-worm', though the true Glow-worm is *Lampyris noctiluca* (see page 78). The light produced is a form of luminescence, being entirely self-produced, and not as is sometimes stated, phosphorescence, which needs the stimulation of some other light source. Just why it is produced is something of a mystery. As centipedes are quite blind and light is usually only produced after stimulation by touch such as finger tickling, or an attack from ants, it seems likely that its purpose is protective rather than a sexual attractant.

Earthworms

As a group, earthworms have been largely neglected in recent times, but they were recognised by Aristotle as being beneficial as long ago as the fourth century BC. More recently, in 1777, the great naturalist observer Gilbert White of Selborne realised their worth to the gardener, and Charles Darwin even wrote a book about them so impressed was he by their industry and importance as tillers of the soil and recyclers of vegetation. Every gardener today is fully aware of their worth and will try very hard not to kill them. In nature the importance of the earthworms is far greater than their apparent numbers would lead us to believe. Many animals rely on them as food, and Badgers, Foxes, Moles, shrews, Hedgehogs and other mammals all take them, sometimes in large quantities; even such an unlikely predator as the Tawny Owl feeds exclusively on earthworms on occasion. There is no doubt that the countryside and all it contains would be a different place without them.

Earthworms cannot survive for long in the light and dryness of day, for their skin is covered with a thin film of slime which allows water to pass from the body at a rapid pace if exposed. As such they are animals of the soil where they can find food and are protected from water loss, and only come to the surface on damp days or during the relative safety of the night. Cold nights, however, are almost as lethal to them as dry days; windy nights are also to be avoided by the worm watcher, as air currents increase the rate of evaporation and keep worms underground. One might wonder why they bother to come to the surface at all, but not all their food is in the earth and they

Fig 18 Earthworms regularly come to the surface to collect food; leaves may often protrude from the burrow entrance

need to replenish stocks from time to time. Often worm burrows have leaves protruding from the entrance hole; these have been dragged in by the worm which gradually pulls them in further as the tips are consumed. Perhaps the most important reason for coming to the surface, however, is to find a mate, the chances of coming across another worm when confined within a fairly distinct burrow being somewhat remote. At certain times of the year, when the weather is warm and humid, lawns and other areas of vegetation are strewn with pairs of worms half exposed from their burrows and united by a band of slimy mucus secreted from the saddle (clitellum). This is not, as is often believed, evidence of a worm having been cut in two and the two halves joined together again, though such regeneration is a well-known phenomenon. Incidentally, worms cannot be for ever cut into pieces each of which will form a new worm; there is a limit to the number of times this can be done, which varies from species to species.

Because earthworms are so sedentary and easy to watch they make an ideal group to study, and it is surprising that so little is known of their ways and preferred habitats. Even simple distribution tables are still lacking for many of our species. Like other animals, they avoid competition with each other by living in different environments; the largest of our species

Lumbricus terrestris is, for example, common in most gardens. The 'brandling' much favoured by anglers is, as its name *Eisenia foetida* would suggest, often found in manure heaps. Others are found in leaf litter, sandy soils and even living underwater at the sides of streams. Glowing earthworms are occasionally reported although I have never witnessed this phenomenon myself. It is thought this may be due to luminous particles in the slime resulting from the earthworm's own metabolism, or more likely a residue from luminous bacteria or fungi which the worm has eaten. Whatever the cause it is worth looking out for, and photographing.

Slugs

The abhorrence with which slugs are regarded was forcibly brought home to me after I had taken part in a natural history radio programme. I had spent much time on my hands and knees in ditches and in turning logs and stones, in search of slugs to watch and photograph. Wanting to share this new-found fascination, I found myself on the air extolling the virtues of these molluscs and their beauty of patterning, sculpturing and colour. The next few weeks saw me as the local slugs' champion, defending them over the 'phone, by letter, in the street and even while having a quiet drink in a remote pub – everybody it seems hated slugs. I find this very sad, for a few nights spent among the damp leaf litter will reveal one of the most colourful groups of animals in Britain.

Although slugs possess the elongated 'foot' of the snails and the eye-bearing 'tentacles', they do not have the coiled visceral hump protected by a shell. To regard slugs as shell-less snails is, however, quite wrong. Many slugs do in fact possess at least a vestige of this structure in the form of a plate or collection of calcareous granules carried internally within the body; and three British species of slugs – the so-called 'shelled slugs', all belonging to the genus *Testacella* – still retain an external shell, much reduced though it is. Reduction or loss of shell has obvious advantages for animals which tend to make their homes in narrow crevices or feed beneath the soil on roots or other subterranean matter, and presumably this greater ease of food gathering outweighs any disadvantages. The *Testacella* are the sole representatives of their family in this country, so distinguishing them is not difficult. The other three families are without external shells and, since size and colouring is very variable and the taxonomy of slugs as a whole is far from clear, in some cases it may be necessary to dissect the animal to achieve positive identification. There are, however, a few guide-lines. Close study of a slug will reveal a mantle pore – a hole in the side which opens and closes as the animal breathes. In the family Arionidae, the pore is situated in front of the middle of the mantle shield. The Arionidae also lack a keel along the body and thus have a rounded cross-section. The remaining two families, the Milacidae and Limacidae, have the respiratory pore behind the middle of the mantle shield towards the back of the animal. These two families do possess a keel; in the former it extends the whole length of the 'tail' from mantle edge to tip, in the latter it is restricted to the tail tip and rarely reaches to the back of the mantle. The Milacidae

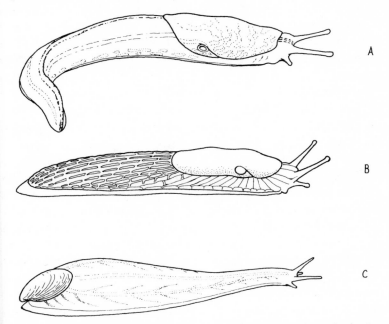

Fig 19   The position of the mantle pore and the possession of a keel or shell help to identify slugs: A Limax; B Arion; C Testacella

are also distinguished by possessing a horseshoe-shaped depression on the top of the mantle shield.

Slugs are ideal subjects for study, being both slow moving and usually conspicuous. It is surprising, therefore, that they have too often been dismissed as enemies of the gardener without much thought being given to their food or habitat preferences. What little systematic work has been carried out reveals that they are not all pests. Perhaps the most carnivorous are the shelled slugs – the testacellids – which impale their prey, usually earthworms or other slugs, by their tooth-bearing radula before devouring them. The Milacidae are undoubtedly frequent pests of root crops, especially where found in large numbers; the Garden Slug must also be regarded as a competitor for garden produce and its commonness makes it a serious pest, while *Deroceras hortensis*, probably our most numerous slug, likes seedlings and other green plant material. Many slugs, however, are quite harmless feeders on algae, fungi and decaying vegetable matter.

Although little is known of the behaviour and habits of our slugs, observations have been made on their mating habits and these reveal a fascinating range of courtship behaviour. The most spectacular is that exhibited by the species *Limax maximus*, where the copulatory act takes place while the two slugs are suspended from a branch or other overhanging surface by means of a slender thread of mucus. Others perform sophisticated courtship rituals which include circling each other and licking prior to copulation. Slugs are hermaphrodite.

Slugs are a good example of nocturnal fauna, showing as they do that the problems of desiccation and predation due to slow movement can be overcome to a great extent by normally being active only at night. Slugs are to be found at all times of year but they become less active or seek hiding places during periods of intense cold or drought; excessive rain or wind also deter them. The best slug-watching conditions are when it is warm, still and damp, so that early autumn or late summer are perhaps the best times of year. All slugs are sensitive to light and will retract or curl up in the beam of a powerful torch; a red filter is thus essential for long periods of study.

6 REPTILES AND AMPHIBIANS

Slow-worms and Adders

Reptiles are usually associated with sunny banks where they bask in the heat so necessary for their existence. Being reliant upon this external source and unable to generate their own warmth would seem to preclude these animals being nocturnal, but two of our reptiles – the Slow-worm and the Adder – are regularly abroad at night in a variety of habitats.

The Slow-worm, which is neither slow nor a worm, is really a legless lizard which may grow up to about 305mm (1ft) in length. During the day it can be seen basking, but more often than not it will be hidden under a stone. Its favourite food is the small white slug which is often a pest in gardens. Since slugs do not usually emerge in the heat of the day, the Slow-worm has to come out when they do, and at dusk after rain is a very good time for Slow-worm watching.

The Adder is a true snake and indeed the only British species to have a venomous bite, although this is rarely serious to healthy, adult humans. The snake will normally avoid contact and try to get out of the way rather than attack. The venom is however used when catching its varied prey – lizards, small mammals, frogs and many other types of animal of convenient size. In common with other reptiles the Adder needs the heat of the sun to 'recharge its batteries' and indeed is often seen during the day basking on a patch of bare earth, but the slit pupils of its eyes show that it has the sight adaptation of a nocturnal hunter.

Newts, Frogs and Toads

All our amphibians are nocturnal to some degree, especially when on land. The fact that they spend a great deal of their time out of water surprises many people, but they only need water of any depth during the breeding season as a place to lay their eggs. During the remainder of the year they hide by day under a stone, log or in a hole in the ground and, as might be expected, are at large looking for food when moisture in the air is at its highest and the risk of desiccation is lowest, that is during the night. Also much of their food – spiders, slugs and worms in particular – are active during the hours of darkness. They never, however, stray from damp places near water.

Of our tailed amphibians, the newts, the largest species is the Great-crested or Warty Newt which may attain a length of 150mm (6in) and is distinctively dark purple-brown on the back and yellow-orange on the underside. During the breeding season the male has a high denticulated crest along its back and tail, with a gap just behind the back legs. The Smooth Newt on the other hand has a lower, similarly denticulated, crest which runs uninterrupted along its whole length. The Palmate Newt, our third species, is distinguished during the breeding season by its webbed hind feet and the filamentous tip to the tail. Out of the breeding season the Smooth and Palmate are difficult to tell apart and the females are always virtually impossible to distinguish without very close examination.

Sight is very important to newts in finding food on land and generally moving prey, which may include other newts, is sought. As might be expected from its granulose skin, the Warty Newt is a distasteful species; it does in fact secrete a form of poison sufficient to deter most predators.

Like other amphibians, newts are found in abundance in ponds in early spring when mating takes place. Their courtship rituals are well worth watching, as they include much chasing by the males followed by a complicated ritual dance where the male curves his body in front of the female and vibrates his tail. Spawn is laid singly with each egg wrapped in its own leaf of pond weed, unlike the strings or masses associated with Toads and Frogs. The young newtpoles are very similar to the adults, and the complex metamorphosis involving massive body changes seen in other amphibia does not occur.

Regarding our tailless amphibians, there have been some additions, but these are relatively localised and have not spread much from their points of introduction. The only two native British species likely to be encountered at all commonly are the Common Frog and the Common Toad; a third species, the Natterjack, is now extremely rare. There should be little difficulty in distinguishing between the Frog and the Toad. The adult Frog's back legs are much longer than its front ones, and because of this its mode of progression is different from

Fig 20 The warty skin of the Common Toad provides it with some protection as well as distinguishing it from the Common Frog

that of the Toad – it habitually hops whereas the Toad rarely hops and is much more comfortable when walking. The Toad, like the Warty Newt, has a warty dry-looking skin capable of secreting poison, and thus gains some protection from enemies; the skin of the Frog is smooth and shiny and appears much thinner. Although both species spend much time hunting on land, the Toad is the more terrestrial of the two and as such has a more flattened, stocky body compared with the angular outline of the Frog. Both species need to return to water to breed and do so in the early spring, although frogspawn can be seen in ponds as early as January in the south of the country. Toads generally spawn a few weeks later.

Unlike the newts, the Common Frog and Toad tend to be faithful to the same pond in which they were born, or at least developed, and make annual migrations back to it to breed no matter where they have spent the intervening years – three for the Frog, up to six for the Toad – which it takes to reach maturity. In some parts of the country many of these migrating amphibians meet their deaths on roads which have been built across their traditional migration routes. I know of one such stretch of road, locally known as 'Flat-frog Lane', where every year hundreds are squashed by cars despite the efforts of people to help them on their way.

How these animals find their way back to their ponds and just what decides that a particular pond is a good place to breed, is a question which has baffled scientists for years. A peculiar combination of chemicals in the plants and the water may guide them, as may the stars; but there is much more work to be done to unravel this mystery of our commonest amphibians.

It is just as well that these and other amphibians have benefited from the garden-pond explosion which has opened up sanctuaries where they are welcome; in the wild there is little doubt that their numbers are dwindling as a result of ponds being filled in and the widespread use of pesticides. Nevertheless, it is always worth looking at damp ground or the area around a pond at night, as such places generally have these animals close by.

Page 107 (*above*) The dampness of darkness allows Frogs and other amphibians to move freely without fear of desiccation while searching for food; (*below*) the owl commonly found in town parks is the Tawny Owl

Page 108 The soft plumage of the Barn Owl serves to quieten its flight when in pursuit of prey; the facial discs channel sound to the ears hidden beneath the feathers and aid the bird in locating targets in almost total darkness

7   BIRDS

Very few birds are totally nocturnal. Some are partially night living, but the majority are purely diurnal, which seems odd when we consider that the majority of mammals are perfectly capable of living in darkness. Why should an otherwise successful group of animals miss out on the abundant food supply available at night? The answer is that the basic design of birds is highly unsuitable for nocturnal activity, especially when it comes to the senses needed for food capture and predator avoidance.

Apart from bats, birds are the only vertebrates which fly; but unlike bats they do not have sophisticated sonar to enable them to see in the dark. In fact, they have made physical sacrifices to enable them to take advantage of their aerial environment. In terms of energy, flight is very expensive and the more cheaply it can be achieved the better, so weight has been reduced to an absolute minimum – hollow bones, no teeth in the skull, no long bony tail – to this end. Of particular importance they have dispensed with 'excess baggage' in the form of the organs of smell, but to make up for the loss of this valuable sense the birds have developed acute senses of sight and hearing, and it is on these that they rely for their information about the environment in which they live. Birds have taken a sort of evolutionary gamble, and very successful they are too. Those birds which are very definitely birds of the night – living and feeding in the hours of darkness – have undergone a series of modifications to the bird blueprint, depending on the life-style of the particular bird.

Some waders which probe the mud for food have a very sensitive sense of touch, while the Corncrake and other largely terrestrial birds have acute hearing which enables them to search out their prey yet avoid being captured themselves.

Owls

Finding Food

The most aggressively obvious and mobile birds of the night are the owls; and they are perfectly adapted to cope with the problem, common to all active, nocturnal, flighted predators, of finding food without being detected. It is often said that owls can see in the dark and when you watch an owl hunting or flying fast through the branches of a tree it is easy to believe that this is the case. Owls certainly have very good vision and can see very well in light levels that would leave us blind, but all sight is reliant upon some light and owls are no more capable of vision in total darkness than we are. As a first essential for nocturnal vision, however, owls, in common with some nocturnal mammals, have large eyes. The opening into the eye is large to allow light in, and the large pupil is backed up by a large lens which, in turn, has a long focal length to use light to best advantage. All in all, the owl's eyes are enormous

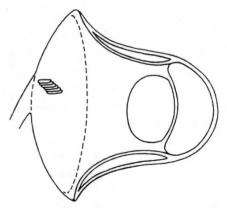

Fig 21   Cross section of an owl's eye. Enlargement of the eye to increase its light-gathering capacity has resulted in a tubular shape; tubular eyes cannot be rotated in their sockets, but owls have overcome this problem by being able to rotate their heads almost a full circle

which, other things being equal, could lead to an increase in weight which would be counter productive for a flying predator. But they also have a conical structure which allows for the necessary focal length without sacrificing lightness as a normal spherical eye would. A conical eye has its own immediate problem in that it cannot rotate in its socket and would normally restrict vision to a forward direction only, but the owls are not too disadvantaged by this as they have the remarkable ability to rotate their heads in almost a complete circle. Because of this, the owls have far better all-round vision than most animals.

Excellent light-gathering capacity is not the whole story, however. Investigations, carried out in America by R. S. Payne, to elucidate the visual capacities of owls and determine which other senses were used to locate prey when light levels fell below the limits of even an owl's acute vision, have revealed that hearing is as important, and sometimes more important, than sight. The experimenter 'cheated' the owl by using a wad of paper which was pulled through leaf-litter in a darkened chamber. The owl could not see the paper, the paper itself had no smell of prey on it, and it was the same temperature as its surroundings. It was thus established that the owl was not using vision, sense of smell or infra-red heat detection, and there is nothing in the owl's anatomy which suggests the possession of an ultrasonic emitter as possessed by the bats, even though many people have spent a great deal of time looking for one. This left either an unknown and mysterious sense, or sound. The sound hypothesis seemed more likely, so loudspeakers were buried beneath the leaf-litter and made to transmit the sounds of a small mammal moving on the woodland floor. The owl performed admirably and struck the target with uncanny accuracy. The experiment was further refined in order to find out how accurate the owl's direction-finding and ranging abilities were. This was done by causing the owl to turn off the sound as it left the perch, thus depriving itself of a 'homing' signal. The owl would have to gain a precise bearing on its prey before leaving the perch if it were to make a successful strike – it proved itself quite capable of doing just that.

Any animal which uses sound to such a degree of accuracy must have a very sophisticated hearing mechanism; a look at the hearing organs of the owl reveals that to be the case. The ears of the owl are placed beneath the feathers on the side of the head, and as with other birds there is no pinna (external ear) as found in the mammals. The pinna is used for direction finding, and you only have to look at your cat or dog to see how mobile it is as it scans the air for sounds. The owls, though, do have a means of perceiving such information. Their ears are placed unequally at the sides of the head, one slightly above the other so that the intensity and angle of sound coming to each ear is slightly different. Owls are able to compute these slight differences and thus gain valuable information about the direction and distance of their prey. In addition the facial discs, which give owls their bespectacled appearance and might seem to be to do with sight, act like radar dishes and concentrate sounds towards the owl's ears. The more nocturnal species of owl have larger facial discs, indicating greater reliance on sound.

These modifications ensure that the owl is capable of detecting its prey in conditions of low light. Equally important is making sure that the prey does not detect the owl; after all flight can be a noisy business and the hearing of many small mammals is acute. The owl is superbly designed for quiet hunting at night. Its size in proportion to its wing area is relatively small, and so it does not have to flap its wings as much as some other birds in order to keep aloft. Owls, too, glide for long distances. The shape of the wings is also important. Those of the more nocturnal species are broad and rounded and allow for a high degree of manoeuvrability – essential to a woodland species constantly at risk from collision.

The structure of the wing feathers themselves are also different from that of day-flying birds, most of which have little need of silent flight. The wing feather of an owl is a lovely object to hold. It is soft and velvety to the touch, and close examination reveals that there is a fine pile-like covering over the surface – a covering which absorbs the sound of the wing's beating against the air during flight. Air rushing over

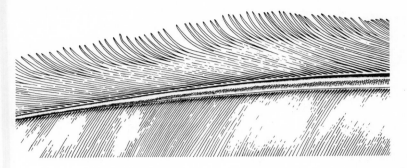

Fig 22   A further aid to silent flight of an owl is the comb on the leading edge of the flight feathers; air is disturbed and caused to flow over the wing with barely a whisper

the surface of the wings is also a potential source of noise, as anyone who has moved a stick quickly through the air and heard the swishing sound it makes will know. To counter this, on the leading edge of the flight feathers are a series of fine combs which interfere with the air-flow, causing it to pass freely and silently over the wing surface. Similarly the legs are covered with feathers to add further sound dampening. All in all, whereas during darkness most birds are either grounded or blunder about noisily at their peril, the owls have a mastery of the night that is second to none.

Species of Owl

Of the ten or so species of owl recorded as occurring in Britain, only five are at all regularly seen or can be regarded as common – the Barn Owl, Tawny Owl, Little Owl, Long-eared Owl and Short-eared Owl. The other species are all rare vagrants which appear only from time to time, the one exception being the Snowy Owl which is now established in Shetland and is also occasionally seen on the mainland. When this occurs there may be confusion with the Barn Owl; the Snowy Owl is, however, a much larger bird, being almost 610mm (2ft) long compared with the Barn Owl's 380mm (15in) and largely diurnal in its habits.

Barn Owl

All five commoner species of owl can, in some lighting conditions, appear light in colour, but only the Barn Owl exhibits white under plumage and honey-coloured upper feathering. Also the large facial discs of the Barn Owl are distinct enough to distinguish it. As its name suggests, it is associated with farmland and although agricultural 'improvements', including loss of suitable roosting sites as old barns and other buildings are pulled down to make way for newer structures, have contributed to its decline in recent years, the Barn Owl is still to be seen in most parts of the country and in some areas is a familiar sight at dusk as it patrols its territory in search of prey. Open fields are a favourite place for hunting and the owl may well have a regular beat, especially where it can follow streams or drainage ditches. Unfortunately roadside verges are also suitable habitats for its prey of small mammals and many of these fine birds meet their deaths on our roads.

As might be expected with an owl hunting in open country, the major prey species is the Field Vole – that small mammal of agricultural and other open habitats. The second most important species, depending on the time of year and habitat, is either the Common Shrew or the Woodmouse, the former becoming more important when it is plentiful in the summer.

Tawny Owl
This is undoubtedly the most widespread owl in Britain. Also known as the Brown Owl and the Wood Owl, its common names reflect its coloration and preferred habitat. It is perhaps the most thoroughly nocturnal of all our species and as such its plumage is not often fully appreciated in the darkness; but on the upper surface it varies from chestnut through to brown and occasionally greyish, with much spotting and streaking. The under surface is also streaked, but the basic colour is a paler buff. All in all, this is a subtle and lovely creature. Its camouflage comes into its own during the day when the owl hides amongst branches or close to the trunk of a tree. In length it is about the same as the Barn Owl, being approximately 380mm (15in) long. It has, however, a more stocky appearance and its wings are more rounded. As with any night-flying owl the facial discs are well-developed, but they look more like a pair of spectacles than do the heart-shaped ones of the Barn Owl.

Fig 23   The Tawny Owl is superbly adapted for its nocturnal existence: large eyes gather as much light as possible and sensitive hearing enable it to locate prey which is grasped in powerful talons, while a velvety covering to the plumage and feathered feet help it to fly quietly

Woodland is the main habitat of this species, but any area containing large trees may harbour Tawny Owls. They are a common bird of the larger gardens, parks and graveyards of our cities, where their calls (see page 121) are a familiar sound of the night. Hunting in wooded areas ensures that they do not compete directly with the Barn Owl, and rodents which prefer cover are its major prey, the Bank Vole being number one on the menu. The highly nocturnal Woodmouse comes second, with other small mammals supplementing the diet as and when they become plentiful or other food is in short supply. An interesting item in the Tawny Owl's diet is the Mole, which is normally thought of as being exclusively subterranean in its habits; but it regularly occurs in the pellets of this species. Perhaps more surprising is that the Weasel turns up in pellets from time to time.

Like all owls, the Tawny Owl consumes invertebrates at certain times of the year even though the more 'cost effective' sources of energy – the small mammals – are preferred. Normally many insects are taken in addition to the usual food, particularly the larger species such as the Cockchafer. The Tawny Owl also makes use of a most un-owl-like food in the form of earthworms; indeed it alone of the larger British owls eats them on a regular basis. The pellets of a Tawny Owl which has been feeding on earthworms are fibrous in texture and brown in colour due to the large amounts of earth taken in at the same time; and their occurrence is usually associated with periods of high rainfall – just the conditions under which earthworms come to the surface. Such rainy conditions are difficult feeding times for the Tawny Owl, especially if it is trying to catch its normal prey of small mammals which gain great advantage from the sound of the rain interfering with the owl's sensory apparatus. At times like this a plentiful supply of worms is most welcome.

Little Owl

The only other species of owl known to feed at all regularly on earthworms is the Little Owl, our smallest species. This owl is now a familiar sight in many parts of England, but this has not always been so for it is an introduced species originating from central and southern Europe and north Africa, and the first introductions did not succeed in establishing themselves as a viable breeding population. Successive introductions in the late nineteenth and early twentieth centuries were more successful, and the Little Owl is now a fine example of how well an animal can do if introduced into a region where there is no native predator already occupying the same ecological niche.

The Little Owl was not without its enemies, however, and as it increased in numbers so hostility from gamekeepers and others concerned with land management also increased based on little more evidence than that any creature possessing claws, talons, hooked bill or sharp teeth must be an enemy which preyed on game birds and had to be eradicated. Fortunately for the Little Owl, the increase in hostility was matched by an increase in concern from bird watchers and conservationists who argued that the bird was innocent of its crimes and, on the contrary, was probably of great benefit to the agriculturalist as regards pest control. The Little Owl, in fact, became a test case for the whole of conservation, and the foremost ornithological body in the land – the British Trust for Ornithology – instigated a survey into its food-taking habits.

The survey, which was known as the Little Owl Food Enquiry and took place between February 1936 and July 1937, was co-ordinated by Alice Hibbert-Ware (see Further Reading) though much of the material examined was sent in by volunteers from all over the country. Only a brief summary can be included here, but the full results published in *British Birds* magazine provide a fine example of just how such a survey should be carried out. Even today it still stands as one of the most exhaustive of its kind. All the Little Owl's range was covered, including areas rich in game; in all 2,469 pellets were analysed, 76 nests and holes were examined and the contents of 28 gizzards identified. Clearly, the bird did not deserve the villainous reputation it had with game preservers; indeed only three instances of predation on game or poultry were recorded amounting to a total of eight definite and one possible chick remains in the total sixteen months of the survey. Other species of birds were more frequent and included Starlings, House Sparrows, and Song Thrushes; there was no evidence of egg stealing or nest destruction. More numerous than birds were the rodents, including largish rats and rabbits. The single most important group was the insects – the Little Owl was found to be an insect feeder at all times of year, in all types of country, and at all stages of its development. In fact to find a pellet devoid of insect remains was a rarity, and many pellets consisted of little else. Many types of insect were taken, their relative abundance in pellets fluctuating, as they themselves, with the seasons. Five species of insect stood out as being of particular significance: Craneflies, Common Earwig, Ground Beetle, Dung Beetle and Cockchafer. Where a particular species was very abundant it was feasted upon almost exclusively, as was the case with the Cockchafer during its short season, and one pellet analysed consisted of the remains of 343 earwigs. Taken as a group, however, the beetles were by far the most predominant insect food; and in all, 121 species were identified. Other groups of insects, and indeed other invertebrates, also figured quite highly in the diet.

In general the introduction of alien species into any country is suspect, for it is always extremely difficult to predict the effect it may have on the delicately balanced ecological web that has developed over many thousands of years. The Little Owl, however, appears to have found a niche where it acts as a control on insects, many of which are regarded as pests by humans. It seems to be doing little if anything to upset the natural balance. As far as landowners are concerned it ought to be a welcome sight over the farmland which is its preferred habitat.

Long-eared and Short-eared Owls

The two 'eared' owls regularly seen in the British Isles are so called because of the tufts of feathers which protrude upwards from above the eyes and which distinguish them from all our other owl species. Far from being ears, these tufts have nothing at all to do with hearing. They are clumps of feathers which can be raised and lowered at will to reflect the bird's moods, and as such they play an important role in posturing and display. As the names indicates, the tufts of the Long-eared Owl are much longer than those of the Short-eared, and at close quarters this difference makes identification relatively simple. Both species are similar in colour and show the typical owl patterning of brownish-grey above streaked with lighter and darker bands which provides ideal camouflage when amongst vegetation during the day. The plumage on the undersurface is much lighter, being cream coloured in the Short-eared and buff in the Long-eared. In both species it shows much streaking, but only in the Long-eared is the undersurface banded with dark-brown bars.

Generally speaking the two species live in different habitats and, while there are no hard and fast rules, the Long-eared is usually to be found in conifer areas – the smaller stands which occur on heaths and moors being as likely to harbour it as the larger plantations. The Short-eared Owl, on the other hand, is a bird of open country and is to be found on heaths, moorland, fells, sand-dunes and similar places. Differences in habitat preferences have inevitably led to other differences, mainly in body form and habits, both of which can help with identification. The Short-eared Owl, with its longer, more pointed wings, has more the appearance of a diurnal bird of prey; the Long-eared's broader and more rounded wings are rather like those of its major woodland competitor and sometime predator, the Tawny Owl. The roosting behaviour of the two species is also determined by their preferred habitats. Lack of trees in open country has led to the Short-eared Owl becoming a ground nester and rooster, which in turn has led to a slanted stance most unlike the upright one usually associated with owls. The Long-eared Owl, on the other hand, has the true erect posture consistent with its arboreal habits.

Small mammals are the major prey items of both species, and the Field Vole is at the top of the list; the Woodmouse comes a close second in some areas. The Common Shrew is very low on the list as a result of the latter's chosen habitat as regards burrowing and food requirements not being the same as the preferred habitat of the two owls. Availability of prey can have a very marked effect on the numbers and distribution of all animals, including owls. In very cold years when food is either absent or very difficult to find further north, many Long-eared and Short-eared Owls migrate south to the British Isles, and can be seen in quite large numbers in some areas. The winter of 1978–9 was one such year, when 604 Long-eareds and 1,549 Short-eareds were recorded. Winter is thus the best time to see these two species – not only are they more numerous, but they are more easily seen due to lack of vegetation. Availability of prey can also affect the numbers of successful egg layings, and a study of the Long-eared Owl has shown that in bad vole years, the breeding success is drastically reduced. This is not as might be expected, always a result of nestlings starving, but is the effect of abandoning of clutches. In some cases, the birds did not lay eggs at all, for in times of hardship it makes good sense to cut down competition for limited food supplies to enable the fitter birds to breed successfully. Just how the birds decide amongst themselves which is going to lay and which is not, is still to be fully understood. It is likely that the larger and fitter birds are able to pick the better territories, leaving their inferiors little choice but to desert or give up before they start.

Finding Owls by Sound

Although owls are generally birds of the night and thus difficult to see, they can normally be located within their territories by the sounds they make whilst hunting, resting at a casual roost or bringing food to their young. As with most other birds, they have a repertoire of sounds which denote different activities and moods, and inevitably their vocalisations reach a peak immediately prior to and during the nesting season. Some calls are commonly used, but others have only rarely been recorded and much investigation needs to be carried out to find out when and why these calls are made. Aside from informing naturalists of their whereabouts, owl calls can, if properly understood, impart much information as to the territorial boundaries of the birds under investigation, whether they have young or are about to start breeding and details of their numerous activities during the hours of darkness. Many attempts have been made to try and translate the calls of birds onto paper, but as the sensitivity of the human ear is very variable and the interpretation of sounds very subjective, some of these have proved more successful than others. There is no substitute for an experienced ear, careful note taking (perhaps with recordings) and a good memory.

'Tu-whit, tu-whoo' is probably the most familiar owl call and it is certainly the commonest to be heard in the suburbs. Often attributed to a Tawny Owl, this call is in reality two calls – one answering the other – and is emitted by a pair of this species. Perhaps a more accurate way of writing it would be 'hoo-hoo . . . oo . . . hoooooo', the sound usually uttered by the male, followed rapidly by 'kewick' from the female. These sounds are not always uttered in the form of a duet, and either can be heard in the absence of the opposite sex. Many variations on these basic calls are quite common; one which is often heard is a sharp 'whee-whee' repeated every half-minute or so.

The call of the Barn Owl is described as a long-drawn-out, wheezy screech which once heard will never be forgotten. It is easy to understand why this owl has earned the name 'Screech Owl' and why it is the source of much superstition in country districts. Its strangled cry certainly conjures up images of crying banshees come to take away the souls of the recently dead. As with other species of owl, there are a series of other less dramatic calls – hissing, snorting and even the odd pleasant chirrup are heard now and again. Similar calls emanate from the Little Owl, depending on its activities and moods; but the commonest call is a repetitive 'wheee-you, wheee-you' or 'kiew-kiew'.

Both species of eared owl are generally silent except during the breeding season, when the Long-eared produces a muffled 'wooo-oooo' which has been described in H. F. and G. Witherbys' *The Handbook of British Birds* as 'a cooing moan rather than a hoot'. This species also uses a sound not unlike the sharp note of the Tawny Owl. The Short-eared Owl produces a variety of short sounds which are often repeated and have been described as 'ough-ough', 'keaw-keaw', 'kwawk' and 'tyak' – the latter two calls sounding more like those from a member of the crow family than those of an owl.

All species produce sounds which are not true vocalisations, but which serve equally important purposes. Expressions of anxiety and alarm, for example, often take the form of bill-snapping or wing-clapping. Many other sounds have been described, but their meanings are often obscure and little understood. Owls obviously have a complex 'language' which is ready and waiting to be deciphered.

Digestive Process

Owls, in common with other birds, do not possess the chewing and grinding mechanism, the teeth, which enables mammals to cope with hard food. Birds which do need to grind food have another way of doing it. Seed eaters, for example, have an extensible pocket of the stomach − the gizzard − which is well furnished with muscles and which often contains pebbles or grit swallowed by the bird. This organ in effect takes the place of teeth in grinding down the food to obtain the useful nutritional substances. In carnivorous birds the gizzard lacks a strong musculature and does not contain grit or pebbles − another example, incidentally, of the modifications towards lightness so necessary in a bird which spends much time on the wing. In these birds the gizzard is merely an extensible sac within which the food is broken down more by the digestive juices than by attrition.

But whether seed eaters or carnivores, the delicate inner surfaces of the alimentary tract need some protection against the indigestible food the bird may swallow such as bones, teeth, hair, feathers and the hard outer skeletons of insects. The gizzard acts as a trap for these fragments and prevents them from travelling any further within the alimentary canal. Inevitably there will be a build up of these fragments and the bird has to rid itself of them from time to time. It does this by producing a pellet.

Finding Pellets

Pellet ejection is, as we have seen, a normal part of life for many birds and, in the case of owls, two pellets per twenty-four hours is the norm for many species. The time and place of ejection, however, varies even within the same species, thus a thorough knowledge of a particular owl and its habitat is necessary before meaningful pellet collection can begin. Collection is easier for some owls than others and the majority of published analyses of pellets has been carried out on those of the Barn Owl because of its convenient habit of producing one of its pellets regularly at the daytime roost where it can be easily collected. The second pellet is ejected somewhere within its territory, usually at one of its casual roosting places used during the night. Unfortunately, the commonest owl of built up areas, the Tawny Owl, is not so considerate to the naturalist, and casts its pellets in any number of casual resting places while hawking its territory. As if that were not awkward enough, the Tawny Owl's pellets are far more friable and delicate than the hard shiny, black pellets of the Barn Owl. More often than not they disintegrate on their journey to the ground, thus making retrieval extremely difficult. The Short-eared Owl also produces pellets anywhere within its territory; the Long-eared on the other hand has more in common with the Little Owl in that they both regularly eject pellets at the daytime roost and also at the site of the hunting perches situated at intervals around their territory.

Where the owls use the same site for pellet ejection, vast mounds can accumulate representing many weeks or months of the bird's food intake. Many published accounts of investigations into the food of owls are based on these caches and, as we have seen, much information has been gained. But, though useful, such studies are limited by not containing more precise details with regard to dating and the number of owls involved; a little extra effort on the part of the pellet collector would have provided a much more useful set of data. When the location of a regular pellet site is discovered, all the existing pellets should be cleared and retained for further analysis as back-up material to the main study. Once clear of pellets, any further castings can be dated with accuracy, depending on the frequency of the collecting visits. Once per day will give the most precise data but, as this often proves impossible, weekly or even monthly visits are acceptable.

It will not be long before you become totally immersed in

the day to day life of your owl. What did it have for supper and what will it have for breakfast? The owl will become part of the family. Many a time when my owl has not produced his pellet, I have spent the interval until he did wondering what had happened to him, whether he left home or had an accident. And as time goes by a picture begins to emerge of the seasonal variations in the feeding habits of the owl due to a number of influences — seasonal fluctuations in numbers of prey species, amount of cover available to those species making them harder or easier to catch, and even the seasonal preferences of the owl itself. If you have time, a further sophistication of owl-pellet study is to compare the food intake of two owls from different territories or, even better, from different habitats. Results from such a study will reveal much about both the preferences of owls and the habits of the prey.

Dissection

The actual dissection of pellets is relatively simple and, as the pellets do not smell, is something which anyone can have a go at. With a little practice it does not take long to become an 'expert'. Although most pellets will come apart quite easily, it is usually advisable to dampen them first to soften them and to allow the bones to be extracted without damage. The first few pellets should be dissected thoroughly and all fragments removed for identification. Only by doing this will you gain an idea of just how complete a record the pellet can contain. Also the fragments will provide the start of a reference collection with which you can compare problematical bones in the future. After a few pellets it becomes unnecessary to remove all the fragments for analysis and you concentrate on the most important ones — the skulls and jaws, the pelvic girdles and the shoulder blades. These latter bones are important because the heads of prey are often bitten off and disposed of, especially if there are young in the nest. You should, however, always scan the remaining material to check for any fragments you do not recognise; they may belong to an animal you have not come across before and which may not be immediately obvious. A particular look out should be kept for amphibian and bird material which sometimes appear in the pellets.

Page 125 (above) All owls produce pellets but the Barn Owl is the most regular in where the pellet is deposited; a study of pellets can reveal a great deal about the diet of a particular individual and also give an indication of the mammals within its territory; *(below)* some of the bones from a dissected Barn Owl pellet – teeth of a white-toothed shrew and the Woodmouse can be clearly seen

Page 126 (above) Often abroad during the hours of darkness, the long-necked Mute Swan is a grazer on water plants; *(below)* many species of duck including Mallard feed or roost on inland waters during the night

Analysing the Results

Having identified the various skeletal elements, it is relatively simple to estimate the numbers of animals involved. All you have to do is count the numbers of the various items and take the maximum they represent as the total. The maximum is taken for two reasons. Firstly skulls and jaws, as we have seen, may be missing; secondly the odd fragment is occasionally left behind in the bird's gizzard to be ejected in the next pellet. As an example, a Field Vole count from a pellet may reveal two skulls, two left lower jaws, one right lower jaw and three pelvic girdles. This represents a maximum number of three Field Voles. Using the skull evidence alone would have produced a maximum of two and would have been inaccurate. The same process is carried out for each species and, when the analysis is complete, you should have the diet of the owl for the previous night (or half of it for those species which eject two pellets per night). The more pellets you collect and analyse the greater will be your knowledge of the owl's diet. Soon you will be in a position to state with some certainty just what your owl feeds on and when it eats it.

In order to make this numerical data more useful, it can be expressed as a percentage of all prey taken. In this way it becomes obvious which are the major species at different times of year, and for different species of owl. Of course it is simpler to express the data in pure numbers, but a look at possible prey species will show that there is tremendous variation in the size of the animals consumed. In pure numbers, one shrew and one rat would have equal status, whereas their weights taken into account would paint a totally different picture. The estimation of weight from skeletal elements is virtually impossible, but H. N. Southern in his pioneer study of the prey of the Tawny Owl recognised this problem and created the following method of representing weights by means of prey units. Even this method is not entirely accurate as it does not take into account the seasonal and sexual fluctuations in weight of the species concerned. However, despite its drawbacks, it is a much used way of making more sense of the data obtained from pellet analysis. It is a convenient method and was never intended to be a hundred per cent accurate; all such data

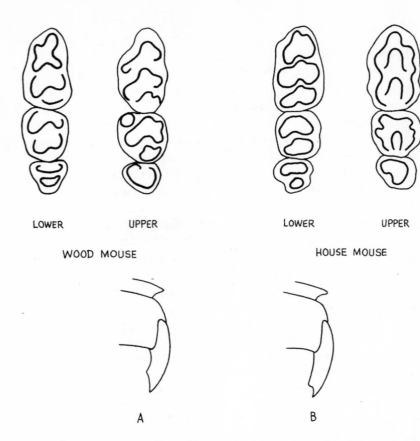

LOWER UPPER LOWER UPPER

WOOD MOUSE HOUSE MOUSE

A B

Fig 24 The tooth surface patterns of mouse teeth and the shape of the incisors distinguish the Woodmouse (A) from the similar House Mouse (B)

should be taken as approximations.

Working on average weights of all the prey species throughout the year, Southern gave each of the commoner species a value expressed in prey units. Thus mice and the smaller voles, which are among the commonest prey and similar in size, are given a value of 1. All other species are based on this standard, so that the smaller Common Shrew is given a value of 0.5; the much larger Brown Rat is given a value 5. These values remain constant for each species and are used as a factor by which the total numbers of each species can be represented. Simply multiply the number of each prey item by its prey-unit value, and a more valuable set of figures will be obtained.

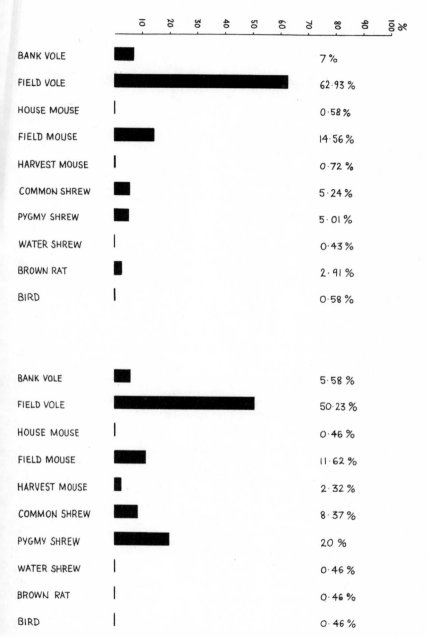

	%
BANK VOLE	7 %
FIELD VOLE	62·93 %
HOUSE MOUSE	0·58 %
FIELD MOUSE	14·56 %
HARVEST MOUSE	0·72 %
COMMON SHREW	5·24 %
PYGMY SHREW	5·01 %
WATER SHREW	0·43 %
BROWN RAT	2·91 %
BIRD	0·58 %

	%
BANK VOLE	5·58 %
FIELD VOLE	50·23 %
HOUSE MOUSE	0·46 %
FIELD MOUSE	11·62 %
HARVEST MOUSE	2·32 %
COMMON SHREW	8·37 %
PYGMY SHREW	20 %
WATER SHREW	0·46 %
BROWN RAT	0·46 %
BIRD	0·46 %

Fig 25   The preferred or available prey of a Barn Owl can be established by pellet analysis: the lower graph shows the species represented as percentages of the total number of animals, while the upper graph shows the same results converted into prey units to give a more accurate picture

The Nightjar

Night-hawk, Dorr-hawk, Churn-owl, Wheel-bird, Goat-owl and Goatsucker are just some of the country names given to this most vociferous bird. Sadly it is not as common as it used to be, but it is still widespread in some regions and its song can be heard in areas of woodland with clearings and on heaths, moors, hillsides, sand-dunes and other wild open places with cover. Cover in the form of heather and bracken or òther low vegetation is essential for this species, as it is a ground nester. The colour of the Nightjar's plumage is fairly typical of nocturnal or crepuscular species which remain concealed throughout the day and is a remarkable example of camouflage, being grey-brown with subtle streaking and spotting which render the bird invisible against bark and leaf litter.

When calling, the Nightjar will sit along a branch and to all intents and purposes looks like a broken extension of it. The distinctive churring song is usually the first indication of a territory-holding pair and, as some of the bird's names suggest, it sounds like the creaking of a muffled door or a spinning-wheel. It can be heard over considerable distances, but its somewhat ventriloquial quality coupled with the bird's colour and method of perching makes the Nightjar a difficult bird to locate precisely. The song starts about thirty minutes after sunset and continues for an hour or so, only to begin again an hour before sunrise. Calling usually ceases again before sun up, and the birds remain quiet during the day. On a few occasions I have seen Nightjars later in the morning and once spent a couple of hours listening to one churring in the middle of the day in brilliant sunshine.

Night is when these birds really come into their own as they wheel about and chase the insects they feed on. The Nightjar is a superb insect-catching machine and very few escape from its wide mouth with its safety net of bristles on either side. A study has shown that much of what the Nightjar eats is regarded as injurious to crops — Craneflies, Cockchafers, and the Ghost and Turnip Moths are all regular items in the diet, for which the gardener should be thankful.

Nightjar watching is a most pleasant occupation if only because you cannot be disappointed. If you end up not seeing them, you will at least hear them churring their strange but relaxing song. Nightjars are curious by nature and will often come to investigate anything strange within their territory – a characteristic which gave me the finest view I ever had of one. I had arranged to record the song for a radio broadcast and was taken to a prime site by a local ornithologist. Up on the exposed heath the wind was blowing which made recording very difficult, so we decided to conduct our interview in a shallow gully and forget the birds until another day. Halfway through our little chat we were interrupted by a female Nightjar which had come to see what was going on and, no more than 2m (6ft) away, she hovered in front of a full moon for many minutes. Time and time again she came to look at us from every angle until she was satisfied that we were nothing to worry about; eventually she was joined by the male and the churring began. It was an unforgettable experience.

Nightingales, Starlings and Others

Despite its name, the Nightingale is not restricted to the hours of darkness and is really a bird of the day. Like many birds of the day, however, the territorial call of the male can be heard long into the evening and often during the night proper. With its rusty plumage above and pale grey-brown underside, the Nightingale looks like a large warbler; in shape, stance and movements it is rather similar to the Robin. It well deserves the recognition it has received as a songster, and a warm summer evening becomes the more enchanting when accompanied by its unique, fluid song.

Many times I have been told of Nightingales singing at night in areas where these birds are rare or unknown, only to find on investigation that the bird in question was not this species. Many other birds sing well into the night, the commonest being the Robin which can be heard singing throughout the hours of darkness, beneath the street lamps in cities. The Nightingale, on the other hand, is more at home in open deciduous woodland where there is sufficient cover to conceal its ground-level nest and provide food in the form of worms and insects.

Reed beds often resound to the night time songs of various warblers; Reed and Sedge Warblers are commonest, but if you are very lucky the elusive Cetti's Warbler may be in your area. Recent work on this bird suggests that nocturnal singing is a peculiarity of unpaired males. Rather than proclaim their territorial rights during daylight alone, these birds find it necessary to continue doing so well into the night in an attempt to attract a mate. It seems likely that other warblers do exactly the same and nocturnal singing may well prove to be of widespread use to the naturalist in establishing which territories in an area contain unmated males, thus providing more accurate estimates of breeding densities than those obtained from daytime singing alone.

One of the weirdest songs is that of the Grasshopper Warbler, which in all bird books is described as being like that of the grasshoppers from which it gets its name, or like the ratchet of a fishing reel. The first time I heard this song I was completely taken in. I was walking by a favourite stretch of river, when I heard an angler reeling in his line. Being very conscious of the dangers of hidden anglers and their flailing lines as they recast, I waited and waited for the coast to be clear, but still the line was being wound in. Then I remembered the descriptions in the bird books and, sure enough, not more than a few yards away was a Grasshopper Warbler perched on the top of a reed stem, singing his heart out.

The same stretch of river is almost devoid of trees except for three lone, large hawthorns — a favourite site for Starlings to roost. At the same time every night in mid to late summer, they fly in by the hundred from all over the surrounding area, until the three trees seem to bend under the weight of their visitors and every bush and reed has its Starling cargo. Once settled, however, it is not long before the birds erupt in a clamour of sound and move as a single organism to the next tree, almost as if they find it hard to settle in the same place for more than a few minutes — the slightest thing will disturb them. Just how they manage to avoid collision and which bird decides the direction of flight is a mystery, but they seem to manage admirably. Communal roosting has great survival potential. Not only does it provide more pairs of eyes and ears to survey the surrounding area for predators, but it also lowers the odds of being picked out by predators. Being one of many thousands thus confers protection to the individual. Large congregations of any animal, on the other hand, seldom go unnoticed and will attract the attention of other animals out for an easy meal, but nature has obviously got the balance correct. Naturalists are also attracted by these large congregations and there is no better place to observe the intricate flocking behaviour of birds than at a roost. It also provides an easy method of assessing populations within an area.

Waders

There are many birds which, although not nocturnal by choice, are quite capable of becoming active at night should there be a moon or necessity prove strong. Open areas such as estuaries are good places for the bird-watcher, or rather listener, during the semi-darkness. Many times, as I have skirted an estuary on my way home in the middle of the night, I have stopped to listen to birds arriving and looking for food. The area comes alive with sound, and there is nothing pleasanter than hearing and seeing as they probe the mud in the moonlight. As they settle in their ranks and go about their business by the water's edge there is, even if one has been out for hours and is cold and hungry, a wonderful feeling of relaxation. It is the state of the tide, rather than the degree of illumination, which determines when the birds feed. Most waders need shallow water or exposed mud for dabbling and probing and, when the tide is right, an army of birds will amass at the water's edge, some to feed and some to roost, the wheeling flocks flying in low from all directions.

The Curlew is one of the most vociferous of the waders and its warbling cry can be heard long after dusk as, with its long curved bill, it probes the mud for small crustaceans. Where the sea meets the land, black and white Oystercatchers can be seen. This large wader is unmistakable as it feeds amongst the

Fig 26 The Curlew with its distinctive curved bill is just one of the waders which takes advantage of low water to feed and is often seen at night

mussel beds, prising its prey open with its long chisel-like bill. Smaller, but also largely black and white, is the shorter billed Turnstone. As its name suggests, this bird flicks over pebbles, weed and shells in search of shrimps and sandhoppers. Most amusing of the birds on the estuary side, are the Knots. The tightly packed flocks arrive and land right at the water's edge, and in their search for food the birds follow the water line, running backwards and forwards with the little waves. It is as if, like their namesake King Canute, they are trying to keep the tide at bay.

Woodcock and Snipe

Although strictly speaking a wading bird, the Woodcock is far more terrestrial in its habits. Like its close relative, the Snipe, it is largely crepuscular and spends much of the day hidden on the ground in woodland, where its plumage provides excellent camouflage. At dusk it emerges and flies straight and low to its marshy feeding grounds. Its large sideways facing eyes allow it to see in low light and give good all round visibility – very useful to a ground-feeding bird – and its long bill is splendidly adapted for probing the soft ground for earthworms and other invertebrates. Once feeding is complete the Woodcock returns to its woodland fastness by the same route it took to its feeding grounds.

Observation of Woodcock as they emerge, and noting the direction of their flight, will tell you where this route goes and if you station yourself somewhere along it you will be sure of seeing the birds night after night. Normally a Woodcock makes for a woodland ride to give it a clear path out of and into its daytime haunt, and if you watch beside this stretch of the route you will have a clear view at the same time as being under cover. On its feeding grounds the Woodcock is easy to watch, for it shows the typical lack of concern shown of other waders when feeding. If you are in position before the birds approach, they will tolerate you being very close indeed.

The Snipe feeds in similar places to the Woodcock, but it prefers to spend the day in dry open land at the edge of its marshy feeding grounds. It is smaller than the Woodcock and has a characteristic zigzag flight for a few yards when first flushed. Snipe are most easily observed at the edge of muddy-margined pools, and even quite small pools can attract large numbers which, unlike the more solitary Woodcock, feed in small groups.

Herons

A regular visitor to estuaries at dawn and dusk, the Grey Heron is our tallest bird which, even in flight, is distinctive. There is no more elegant sight than one of these birds as it slowly glides in with broad, outstretched wings, trailing legs and long neck tucked between its shoulders after a slowly beating flight from its roost or nest which may be many miles distant. It epitomises all of the good qualities and strategy of the hunter, which the naturalist would do well to emulate – slow deliberate movements, carefully timed so as not to cause disturbance, punctuated by periods of patient, motionless waiting.

Herons are by no means restricted to estuaries and can be

seen along most stretches of water which can provide them with the food they require, mainly fish and invertebrates. They can often be seen on agricultural land hunting for voles and other small rodents. But it is to the estuaries that they turn in the winter when other food is frozen under ice, and here they can be found in large numbers, each heron well spaced from its neighbour to allow space for fishing. When feeding on estuaries, the state of the tide dictates their time of arrival and departure, and thus they may feed at any time of day or night. The nocturnal observer would do well to arrive just before the tide turns and there is still plenty of shallow water near the shore for the herons to wade in.

Night feeding may have advantages for herons in as much as their prey may be more active during the hours of darkness. Although little serious work has been carried out on our native species, investigations on an irregular summer and autumn visitor, the Night Heron, indicate that this may be the case. Watmough (see Further Reading) found that, although Night Herons feed both by night and day, their feeding efficiency was greater during the day in terms of successful captures from attempts at fishing. However the prey captured at night was, on the whole, larger; and so although captures were fewer, the actual food intake was greater.

The Night Heron is, as its name implies, a more nocturnal bird than our resident species and is presumably better equipped for night hunting. But it would be interesting to make comparisons between the food of the Grey Heron at night and during the day.

A third species from the Heron Family which may come the way of the nocturnal naturalist is the Bittern. This, sadly, is a rare bird of reed beds and those of us who do not live near its East Anglian broadland stronghold are unlikely to come across it except by accident. Even in the 'Broads' it is seldom seen, being secretive and skulking in its habits and possessing a plumage which provides perfect camouflage. Fortunately for the naturalist this bird betrays its presence by its territorial call, at its best during the breeding season – a deep, slow booming which carries a considerable distance in the peace and quiet of its fenland home.

Wildfowl

Ducks and geese, as any wildfowler will tell you, are nocturnal at certain times of the year. Some wildfowl habitually feed at night, others which normally roost then are driven by the vagaries of the tides to feed instead, and many are migrant species and undertake a great part of their long flights under the cover of darkness. The same site is not always used both for feeding and roosting, and for closer study, careful observation of the birds' habits is needed to find out where these alighting places are. There is no substitute to sitting by the side of lakes, estuaries and coastal bays observing the direction of arrivals and departures. If the birds are flying inland, it may be to feed or roost – usually in a field, much to the chagrin of the farmer. You can of course enquire of local farmers whether the birds use their land but be prepared for uncomplimentary remarks. The local bird-watching society or wildfowlers' club are also good sources of information and can save you time and legwork. As with the waders, wildfowl feeding on water are best observed in the half-light of dusk or when they come in closer and are less easily disturbed.

As a group, ducks seem far more nocturnal than geese. Why this should be so is a mystery, but lakes, estuaries and canals – indeed any stretch of water – is likely to have its nightshift ducks. One of the most familiar species is the Mallard, a common duck of parks and other urban waters, but equally at home almost anywhere. It is seen both by day and by night, depending on local feeding conditions and the amount of disturbance it suffers. My favourite duck is the little Tufted Duck which, with its distinct black and white plumage, tuft and piercing yellow eye, cannot be confused with any other. The Tufted Duck is one of the group known as diving ducks as distinct from the dabbling ducks. As the term implies they dive under water for their food, which is both plant and animal. Two orange-headed ducks – the Wigeon and the Teal – are also to be seen feeding at night. The former is often on land, grazing grass or grain, the latter feeds on water plants and invertebrates. Distinguishing between the two species is a relatively simple matter, for the Wigeon has a lighter patch running up the forehead and an orange breast, the Teal's breast is much darker.

Two smallish geese which may be confused with each other are the Bean Goose and the Pink-footed Goose, indeed some ornithologists believe they are the same species. Both are winter visitors, the Bean arriving in October and the Pink-footed a month earlier. The two geese are distinguished from each other by the bill and foot colour. The Pink-footed, as its name implies, has pink feet, its bill is pink and black. The Bean Goose on the other hand has orange feet and an orange and black bill. Also the Pink-footed is smaller by four or five inches being about 750mm (30in) maximum. Both species are distinguished from all other geese by the dark head and neck. When the days are short, both may leave for their feeding grounds well before dawn and return to their roosts after dusk. On moonlit nights both may be seen feeding, although they would normally be roosting during the hours of darkness on open water away from their feeding grounds. In the case of the Pink-footed, these roosting flocks may number thousands.

Another small dark-headed, dark-necked goose which feeds at night when the tide permits, is the Brent. It can be distinguished from the previous two species by the much darker head and neck, and the 'ring' of white around the neck. The Brent Goose is a specialist feeder and its wintering grounds are largely restricted to where eel grass can be found. In order to get at this strange underwater plant, one of the few that flower, the Brent up ends much like some ducks, and it thus has to wait until the tide is down. In very harsh winters when food is short this bird will graze on land and, being very fond of winter grain, causes concern to farmers in some areas.

The Mute Swan presents an eerie sight as it sails into view brilliant white against the darkness and, unlike all the other wildfowl I have come across at night, seems totally unperturbed by torch and flashlight. It just stares, its red shining eyes reflecting the light, as if in disbelief at a human about at such a strange hour.

The long neck of the Mute Swan is an adaptation for feeding on plants which grow on the beds of rivers, canals and estuaries. Shallow water is thus a prerequisite which enables the swan to reach this food. Lately swans have come under threat as a direct result of this method of feeding by picking up lead lost by anglers in the form of fishing weights or from wildfowlers shot which has accumulated over traditional wildfowl feeding areas. The RSPB has mounted a campaign to outlaw lead in fishing weights and a number of substitutes are now available which are made of non-lead products. Lead poisoning is now known to have claimed many birds over the last few years but many other deaths may have been less direct than mere poisoning. Lead, even in small quantities, can affect the breeding success of individual birds and many of the birds which collide with overhead cables may have been debilitated by lead and less efficient at manoeuvring whilst in flight.

Moorhens and other Rails

The Moorhen is a familiar sight on canals and ornamental lakes where its apparent lack of concern for human presence is a contrast to its behaviour in the wild. There, like all the rails, it tends to be a shy bird and avoids contact with people wherever possible. Time and time again my presence has been betrayed by its explosive distress behaviour – shooting across the surface of the water with wings beating the surface and repeating its loud 'keh-keh' cries. It always happens when you least expect it and least want it, and is never more frustrating than in the quiet of the night. In fact I was unaware that Moorhens could be nocturnal until I first experienced such a heart-stopping experience. I had always assumed they went to roost during darkness and, while this is normally the case, at certain times of year when there are clear moonlit nights large numbers can be seen feeding on wet meadows. Flocks of twenty or thirty individuals are by no means uncommon outside of the breeding season, and can be seen night after night in the same field. Such large flocks do not pose a great problem to the nocturnal observer as there is usually sufficient light to see them before they see you. It is the odd individuals guarding their territories which are the most sensitive, and which give you away to every bird and mammal in the district if you are unfortunate enough to stumble upon one by mistake.

The only bird which is likely to be confused with the Moorhen is the Coot. Both species share the same general form and colour, but the Coot is the larger of the two – 380mm (15in) as opposed to 330mm (13in) – and lacks the distinctive white tail markings of the Moorhen. At closer quarters and in good light, the bill and frontal shield extending from the bill up between the eyes to the forehead will be seen to be of different colours – white in the Coot and red in the Moorhen. The partially webbed or lobed feet of the Coot are also quite distinctive when seen as tracks, although they are far from obvious when the bird is swimming or walking.

Both Coot and Moorhen eat a variety of foods including vegetation and invertebrates taken on land and afloat, and even thought the Coot is more inclined towards a diet of vegetation there is still possible competition between the two species. One way of avoiding this rivalry is for animals to be separated by differing habitats, and this is exactly what happens with the Coot and Moorhen. The Moorhen tends to frequent more enclosed and smaller stretches of water and is a common sight on drainage ditches, canals and ponds. The Coot, on the other

Fig 27　The shy, skulking Water Rail will be found in reed beds and other areas where there is water and cover

hand, is a bird of more open, larger stretches of water such as lakes, meres and reservoirs.

One of our most beautiful birds, the Water Rail, is rarely seen, so good is the camouflage effect of its plumage. Brown above and grey below, with barring on the flanks, it blends perfectly with the reeds and other vegetation amongst which it makes its home. It is, however, not a rare bird, but is shy and elusive; I have only ever seen one by accident while sitting near reeds waiting for something else to appear. The Water Rail possesses a long red bill which immediately distinguishes it from all other British rails, and it uses this both as a pair of forceps or as a pick to deliver a death blow to its prey. Food is usually invertebrates which it picks up from the surface of the mud it likes to inhabit; but occasionally it will take frogs, small mammals and birds. Muddy areas seem to be the prerequisite for this bird and so Water Rails are usually found in wetlands in the proximity of still or slowly moving water.

Water Rails, being secretive, are difficult to observe and there is still a great deal to be learned about their habits. The young are known to be at least partially nocturnal, and the adults make their migration flights at night so it seems likely that they are more active at night than has been previously supposed. Difficulty of habitat and the darkish coloration of the bird itself have made this difficult to confirm, every opportunity should be taken to establish whether this is indeed a fact.

Another rail, the Corncrake, is largely nocturnal and more often heard than seen, its characteristic grating call reflected in both its English name ('crake-crake') and in its Latin name ('crex-crex'). Wherever this bird occurs the territorial call of the male will be heard throughout the breeding season at night and, once heard, cannot be confused with any other British bird. So characteristic is it that it has been used in breeding surveys as the sole indication of the bird's presence or absence.

Sadly this call is becoming more and more a collector's item, for the Corncrake is becoming rarer as the years pass. Earlier this century it seemed to be on the increase in certain parts of its range, largely because expansion in the use of land for cultivation provided more suitable habitats. The tables have turned, however, and the farming which was responsible for the Corncrake's increase is now responsible for its decline. Larger fields mean a more mechanised type of farming and combine harvesters and other farm machinery have taken their toll; for while the Corncrake's habit of crouching down to avoid danger is very efficient when avoiding its normal predators, it is not effective against the onslaught of harvesting machinery. The nests built in shallow depressions are also at risk. Fluctuations in weather conditions and the birds' habit of flying low and colliding with overhead cables have also been suggested as causes of the decline. There is little doubt that these are contributory factors, but modern mechanical reaping seems to be the major threat. The only two dead Corncrakes I have seen were both well and truly 'reaped'.

Despite its name, the Corncrake is not confined to cornfields, but is in fact more at home in land put down to grazing providing it is not too heavily grazed, when it is in danger from trampling. In general the vegetation should be relatively short, enabling the bird to stretch up and survey its surroundings. With such a shy retiring bird the best method of observation is to wait patiently in a suitable habitat; if the birds are there the distinctive call will soon give them away. So territorial are the males that if the call is imitated by drawing a comb across a piece of wood, they will usually come to investigate their rival.

In colour the Corncrake is similar to the Water Rail, but it lacks the greyish underparts and is very much more chestnut. Though at about the same size [280mm (11in)] it does not have a long red bill.

Page 143 (above) Pipistrelles preparing to leave the daytime roost; *(below)* Brown Long-eared Bats (*Dave Bolton*)

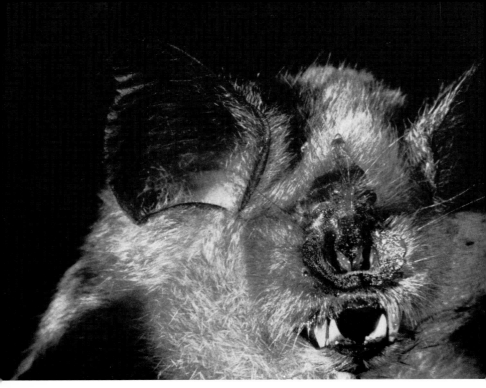

Page 144 (above) The Greater Horseshoe Bat epitomises the ugliness which most people associate with bats; the nose-leaves are essential to this bat's direction-finding mechanism; *(below)* X-ray photograph of Pipistrelle showing the structure of the wings which differs markedly from that of birds

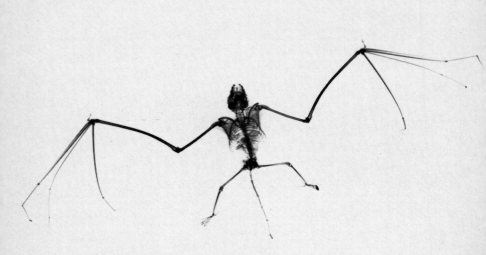

8   BATS

I first noticed bats when I was very young. They were flying around the lamp-posts just down the road in the suburban street where I grew up. I had no idea what sort they were, I didn't even know there were different sorts, I just watched them going round and round catching the moths attracted by the light. Looking back, they must have been Pipistrelles, one of the commonest of our bats and, not surprisingly, this was the first bat I ever held in my hand. Such perfection of form in a creature so small is truly wonderful, and after the first few minutes you begin to realise that the bat in your hand is showing just as much interest in you as you are in it. With open mouth and quivering ears it is taking in the picture of its captor, not with sight but with sound. The more I study bats the more I want to know about them. As creatures of the night they have no equals.

As flying animals, bats are often compared with birds. The birds are, as we have seen, the only other vertebrates to have mastered the aerial environment, and they are often labelled 'the undisputed masters of the air'. Such a title is ill-deserved. There is no doubt that the wings of birds are of better functional design than those of bats. They are constructed of feathers attached to a leading edge of bone, skin and muscle which ensures that the bird wing can sustain a fair degree of damage. A few missing feathers, for example, is no great hardship and new ones will grow at the next moult. The bat's wings are constructed on a totally different principle – a delicate membrane of skin is stretched between the elongate,

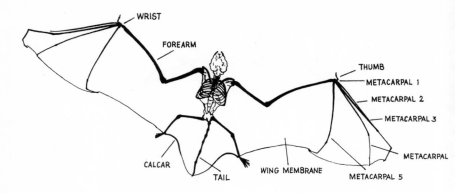

Fig 28 The skeletons of bats reveal the bones which support the thin membranes

fragile fingers of the hand and this membrane is prone to tearing and the bones to breakages. A tear is not always disastrous, and many bats show evidence of injury to their wings; but a serious injury may not heal and then the bat will be unable to fly. Without the power of flight feeding becomes impossible, and the animal will die of starvation.

In this sense, bats' wings are inferior to those of birds; but the flight of healthy bats leaves birds standing. You have to actually watch bats to appreciate the sheer agility of their flight – power dives, breathtakingly quick low-level man-oeuvres, hovering and the ability to make a capture and eat the prey on the wing come easy to them. The intricate tactics necessary for feeding are truly amazing. Scooping tiny insects from the very surface of water, gently picking moths from the blossom of sallows, or a high-speed chase through the branches of trees, all require skills which would seem beyond the scope of such small animals. In addition all this is taking place under the cover of darkness – incredible!

Echolocation

Flying at night requires very special skills and a very keen perception of the immediate surroundings. Birds for instance, mostly reliant on sight, are all but grounded in the dark. Only the owls and a very few others have managed to overcome lack of light to any degree. The facts of how bats manage are now reasonably well understood, but to early naturalists there was no obvious answer.

As early as 1794 Lazzaro Spallanzani, an Italian naturalist, began experimenting with bats in order to unravel the secrets of their phenomenal ability to avoid objects and capture prey. Some of his experiments and those of his contemporaries seem both crude and cruel by today's standards; they did, however, lay the foundations for modern studies. As a human reliant on sight as his major sense, Spallanzani inevitably tested the sight of bats first. Having blinded the unfortunate animals, he found that loss of vision in no way impaired their ability to carry out intricate navigation. The inference was that bats must be endowed with a particularly acute sense of touch and, as the delicate wing membranes were the obvious location for this sense, a bat's wings were varnished. On being released it showed no sign of a decrease in aerial skill, and obstacles and tightly curving passages were negotiated with ease. Similar results were obtained when the tongue was cut out or the nostrils plugged with wax. The answer became obvious – bats had a sixth sense which we did not possess and therefore could not appreciate!

At about the same time a Swiss scientist, Charles Jurine, tested the hearing of bats by plugging their ears with wax. The result was that the bats were unable to navigate successfully. This discovery seemed to produce at least part of the answer and should have led to a breakthrough in research, but this was not to be. A combination of inadequate equipment and overruling scientific dogma led by the eminent and powerful Baron Cuvier was sufficient to cause a postponement of any further enquiries along these lines. It was almost one hundred years before Jurine's work was repeated and his results accepted.

It even took a war to provide the clue to the exact mechanism. The invention of sonar as a means of locating submarines during World War I led Professor Hartridge of Cambridge in 1920 to postulate that bats used sound to locate prey and obstacles. By 1944 an American, Dr D. R. Griffin, and his fellow workers at Harvard University, had repeated all the early experiments and proved beyond doubt that bats made use of high-frequency sound waves beyond the sensitivity of the human ear. As the sound is used for navigation and location of prey, the phenomenon came to be called 'echolocation'. Basically echolocation is the use of a series of pulses of sound which, when they hit something, are reflected back to the bat and tell it all it needs to know about the world into which it is flying.

With research continually taking place, echolocation in bats is becoming less of a mystery; information regarding the types of sound used under different conditions and by different species is slowly being amassed. The pursuit and capture of prey, once it has been located, takes place in under a second, and as such is virtually impossible to observe in the wild; even in strictly controlled conditions and with the most sophisticated camera equipment, the moment is rarely captured. The use of sound equipment, however, has enabled scientists to delve into the fascinating world of high-frequency sound and share the moment of capture with the bats themselves; and the development of portable receivers − bat detectors − which translate the bats' signals into sounds audible to the human ear, has opened up this line of study to the amateur naturalist.

Apart from altering their echolocation calls to suit varying purposes such as navigation and prey capture, different species of bat are now known to produce particular calls by which they can be distinguished with some certainty in the field. In technical terms it is frequency, duration and frequency-pattern changes, measured against time, which distinguish the different bats. In practice it is the recognition of the pitch and nature of the call − whether clicks, chirrups or trilling − which are the greatest help to the amateur. This sounds easy, but it can be most frustrating. There is no readily available set of recordings for the different bats with which to make comparison; also direction of travel, distance from the detector and the nature of the locality all affect the type of signal received. It is only too possible to receive seemingly distinct signals through the detector, but be unable to identify the species while in flight. Another disadvantage of using a bat detector is that you are likely to be stopped by the police. On more than one occasion I have been questioned as to what I was doing in a churchyard in the middle of the night with a strange machine emitting unearthly sounds!

The use of bat detectors is, however, going to revolutionise the study of bats, for there is no doubt that there will be a surge of interest in these creatures over the next few years as a direct result of the availability of cheaper models. But useful though these technical devices are, we must remember that they are only aids, and should not be allowed to take over from the more traditional methods of observation. The state of our knowledge at the moment is the result of generations of naturalists working with only their eyes and unaided ears, and there is still much to be learned in this way – positive identification of many species of bat is, in fact, only possible from visual examination in the hand. Careful observation of bats on the wing even without mechanical devices is still very helpful; and at least the commoner species can be identified with some certainty. A note of warning though regarding the handling of bats; this, except under licence, is now illegal (see page 160).

Fig 29   Bats roost during the day in a variety of places including buildings, caves, hollow trees and bridges

Noctules

The fact that the Noctule is our largest bat was brought home to me quite dramatically when one flew low at no more than a couple of feet above my head. It seemed enormous as it patrolled between the trees on a wooded hillside, its 380mm (15in) wingspan appearing much larger than life against the pale grey of twilight. Seeing Noctules close is not a common occurrence, but they will fly down to have a look if they detect you – a habit which no doubt led to the myth of bats flying into hair. I was treated to an even better view one evening as I walked across a meadow of long grass, disturbing many insects which provided bounty for the Swifts that were screaming through the air. As twilight fell, the Swifts were joined by half a dozen Noctules which shared the feast.

Noctules associating with Swifts is not uncommon, and possibly there is some mutual benefit. Perhaps the bats rely on the Swifts to find congregations of insects, or perhaps being part of a flock gives the Noctules a modicum of protection. Whatever the reason, it is wise to look twice at Swifts flying over open fields, especially near wooded country, for Noctules resemble Swifts in many ways. Not least their flying styles are similar, for both fly high and fast. Their squeaks and screeches, which often continue during flight, are also alike.

Noctules are good bats to begin studying, for apart from their size, which makes them easy to see, they tend to fly other than in the dead of night. Their flight times are geared more to the flight times of their insect prey than to light levels. Their usual emergence is just before dawn for about half an hour, and often again around dusk. But do not be surprised if you see them at other times, as they are known to fly at night and occasionally during the day as well.

The larger insects form the preferred prey of this species and, during May and June, Noctules are often seen flying very low over hedgerows catching the seasonal Cockchafers. When insects of any type are particularly abundant or in short supply, most bats alter their normal patterns; the Noctule is no exception. A glut of beetles or crickets at a refuse dump will tempt these bats away from their normal woodland haunts, just as a dearth will cause them to desert an area or merely stop hunting. On nights of buffeting wind or heavy rain Noctules tend not to fly, this being a symptom of their prey being kept down rather than their own preference.

During the summer months, Noctules spend the day resting in hollow trees, and finding such a roost is a boon to observation. Usually it is given away by the noise the bats make, often at any time of day. Emergence and return times can both be easily monitored, while the direction taken by the bats as they emerge gives an indication of their feeding grounds. If you have a bat detector the tuning dial should be set at 25kHz to obtain the best rendering of their chirruping echolocation calls. If you can see the bats and listen to them at the same time you will really begin to appreciate the usefulness of this instrument. The speaker will almost shatter as the bats fly towards you, and you can even hear that final fast buzz as they close in and capture their prey. During the winter, Noctules can be found in hollow trees and house roofs.

Serotines

The Serotine is much the same size as the Noctule and often reported as flying with that species. There is therefore the possibility of confusion, and it is likely that the Serotine would be found to be more widespread than its present essentially southern distribution, if only identification on the wing could be confirmed. In the air it is slower than the Noctule, but can, like all bats, produce bursts of speed on occasion. Its flight has been described as moth-like, and it is certainly more reminiscent of a giant moth than the Swift which the Noctule so closely resembles. Its feeding habits are essentially similar to the Noctule's, but it prefers open ground in woods where it flies lower, usually without accompanying vocalisation. The frequency of its echolocation pulses is also different. The dial on the bat detector should be set at 40-50kHz, and the sound produced is a series of clicks.

The Serotine uses both trees and buildings for its summer roost, and emerges about twenty minutes after dusk. There does not appear to be a distinct morning flight, and this bat can be seen at all times of the night. Unlike the Noctules, Serotines hunt alone, each having its own hunting territory. Thus a large bat flying quietly and alone through a woodland ride is likely to be a Serotine.

Pipistrelles

Just as the Noctule can be recognised by its size and flight pattern, so can our smallest bat, the Pipistrelle. Although, because of its 230mm (9in) wingspan, in overall area and weight it must be regarded as larger than the Pygmy Shrew, the Pipistrelle is in body length our smallest mammal and rarely exceeds 50mm (2in). The wing beat and consequent flight are best described as rapid and jerky, so that when you see a Pipistrelle in flight it seems as if it is using all its energy to keep aloft and the effort of flying is out of all proportion to its tiny body. It is almost as if it has a constant fight against gravity. Its country name, the Flittermouse, sums it up perfectly.

The Pipistrelle lives in a wide variety of habitats including the centres of our largest cities. It is, as already mentioned, the commonest species in most parts of the country and is usually the one that householders somewhat reluctantly give a home to beneath their facing tiles or in the roof space. The first indication of the bats' presence is likely to be the noise they make as they emerge from their roost. Even the most modern houses can harbour a Pipistrelle colony; I went to one less than a year old which had a colony of thirty! Colonies can be much larger, however, and the gentleman who had counted 80 emerging from his roof at dusk was surprised when we did another count and raised the number to 180. These Pipistrelles do no harm; like all other bats they do not carry disease, and their droppings are dry and do not constitute a health hazard. Fortunately, having heard sounds through the bat detector, most householders become proud that their house has been chosen and they become ardent bat counters. Living with humans brings other problems too, for Pipistrelles are regularly caught by cats. Just how a cat manages to do this was a mystery to me, until I saw one lurking above an exit hole ready to scoop bats from the air as they emerged for the evening flight.

Emergence of Pipistrelles is usually preceded by a lot of scrabbling and chattering, as if many bats are arguing and pushing each other out of the way in an effort to be first out. The first one out is always on his own for the first few minutes then, after a respectable pause, the rest emerge, often in small bunches. Depending on the size of the colony, emergence of all the bats can take a long time. In the colony of 180 already mentioned, it took an hour for all its members to squeeze out of the single narrow entrance. Such a lapse of time can make counting difficult, some bats returning before the others have left.

After emergence and a couple of orientating sweeps of the garden, Pipistrelles go their separate ways, each member of the colony having its own hunting beat, the length of which varies with the locality but normally about 46m (50yd). It usually centres around a favourite tree, building or, as is often the case in cities, a particular lamp-post; and this habit of hawking a regular beat is very convenient for the naturalist. The individual bat can be relied upon to re-appear every few minutes or even every few seconds, such regularity giving more than one chance to identify the species and the opportunity to study aspects of behaviour. The flight duration of the Pipistrelle is variable depending on the time of year and the number of insects available; the state of its young may also have an effect. If they are still being weaned they have to be fed at intervals throughout the night, and hence the adult bat will return several times to the roost. If the young have been weaned, the flight may last much longer. Even within a flight period, however, Pipistrelles will take many rests, usually on a tree or some other convenient object.

The normal food of Pipistrelles is, predictably, the smaller insects, and they can eat many thousands in one night. The Pipistrelle is a good bat for studying food intake. If you find one with a relatively small beat you can follow it for most of its flight, and with the aid of a bat detector the feeding 'zips' can be heard. These are emitted as the bat closes in for the kill and represent a speeding up of the ultrasonic signals. Each 'zip' represents an attempt to catch prey and as such indicates the number of times a bat would like to catch an insect.

Pipistrelles take all their food on the wing, and normally eat it while still flying. Occasionally, however, they will catch something a little too large to cope with, and this will be pouched within the tail membrane in order to manoeuvre it into a better position for eating. Temporary roosts are sometimes used for extra large prey. Favourite places are the lintels of doorways from which the uneaten legs and wings fall to the floor and form a small pile of debris — evidence of the night's feeding by a particular individual.

Long-eared Bats

It is not often that a new species of animal is recognised as part of the British fauna, but when this does occur it is a red-letter day indeed. The odd Grey Long-eared Bat had been recorded in Britain in the early parts of this century, but all sightings were thought to be strays from Europe where it is more numerous. In the 1960s, however, more were sighted, and their position as a resident breeding population established. I have seen this bat in Devon, unfortunately dead as the result of a predatory cat. The locality seemed consistent with the description of its European habitat — lowland, sparsely wooded country with small towns and villages. I have tried to find a roost but have so far been unsuccessful. In retrospect it is not surprising that if a mammal is to be added to the fauna, it should be a bat. After all, bats are nocturnal and hence difficult to see, until recently they have been very difficult to distinguish in flight, and they are not among the most popular of animals. As such they would probably escape the notice of all but the specialist.

The Grey Long-eared Bat is, then, extremely rare, in contrast to the Brown which is very common — in some areas even commoner than the Pipistrelle. The Brown Long-eared is easily distinguished from all other bats, barring the Grey, on account of its disproportionately long ears, which are as long as the head and body combined and reach 50mm (2in). When you first see a Long-eared it is difficult to imagine how it keeps its ears outstretched while in flight. While at rest the long outer ears are folded back out of the way, with only the small pointed 'inner' ears (tragi) remaining erect. This bat should be sought in wooded districts. The more landscaped parts of towns are also worth investigation, and it is often found roosting in house roofs. I was recently presented with an injured specimen which had landed at the feet of a traffic warden, having dropped from a flyover in the centre of a city.

In common with all woodland-inhabiting bats, Long-eared are best seen against the sky rather than the foliage; so station yourself near a tree with fairly open branches. On arrival, Long-eared Bats will be flying close to the ground, but their normal hunting flight is usually much higher depending on the tree and where the insects are flying. Whilst hunting, their flight is slow and fluttering, rather like the moths on which they feed. Long-eared tend to pick insects off blossoms rather than catch them in open flight, and are known as 'gleaner feeders'. This may explain why they appear to have larger eyes, and a better sense of sight, than most bats.

Daubenton's Bat

The habitats of bats can often provide the key to the species, and this is no more so than with Daubenton's Bat. Water Bat, in fact, is its other and very apt name; for it often occurs in the proximity of water. Sitting by a river, canal or large pond on a warm summer evening is a pleasant occupation at the best of times, but it is greatly improved when these bats are close by. Unfortunately, like all bat species they have declined, so that their old haunts only support a few individuals.

Daubenton's Bat is the nocturnal equivalent of the Martins and Swallows, indeed it is often difficult to tell it apart from these aerial counterparts. The dividing line between when the last of the birds leave at dusk and the first of the Daubenton's Bats arrive is often impossible to draw, so similar are they as they swoop, glide, and skim the surface of the water. The wing beat of Daubenton's Bat has been likened to that of the Sandpiper; and the quivering flight rather than deliberate flap, also the habit of flying very low – often barely an inch above the water – is certainly reminiscent of these small waders.

Calm waters at dusk have the same appeal for both insectivorous birds and bats. There is an abundant supply of food, and early evening becomes feasting time as insects emerge from their watery youth or lay eggs at the surface, providing easy pickings for skilful predators. Mayflies and Caddisflies are particular favourites of Daubenton's Bat, so that one of the best places to see it is where there is alder and other dense bankside vegetation. The insects emerge around such greenery in their hundreds, and even large dragonflies and moths may fall victim to these low-level hunter-killers of the water surface.

Horseshoe Bats

All the bats previously described belong to the Vespertilionidae or 'whispering' bats. The horseshoe bats belong to the Rhinolophidae, the only other family represented in the British Isles. There are two species, the Greater Horseshoe and the Lesser Horseshoe, and in the hand or at rest they are easily distinguished from all other bat species by the possession of the bizarre outgrowths of skin above the nostrils, which give them their name. Known as nose-leaves, these are actually made up of three distinct elements. The 'horseshoe' – a shallow cone-like structure – is the most obvious, and encircles the nostrils. Above the nostrils and extending up between the eyes is an erect triangular leaf known as the lancet. Finally growing between the lancet and the horseshoe is a vertical leaf – the sella. Many people seem to assume that all bats have these excrescences, and the ugliness associated with bats is obviously due to these growths. But the nose-leaves are not merely morbid decoration, they have an important part to play in the emission of ultrasonic pulses for, unlike the whispering bats which emit their ultrasonic pulses through the mouth as it is held open in flight, the horseshoe bats channel theirs through the nose. The nose-leaves are crucial to the fine tuning of this signal into an intense beam, which travels further and is more accurate than that of other bats.

The signals of the horseshoe bats are quite distinctive and are easily recognised with the help of a bat detector, which should be tuned to the higher part of the scale as the frequencies emitted by these bats are at the top of the range. The Greater Horseshoe is detected with settings around the 80kHz mark, and the Lesser Horseshoe at the even higher value of around 110kHz. The duration and pulses are also distinctive. Horseshoe bats emit a longer pulse than the whisperers; it lasts about 50millisecs and is of a constant frequency during the main part of the pulse with a rapid build up at the beginning and a trailing off at the end. The resulting sound you hear is described as 'chirruping'. The sound is very bird-like and once heard will never be confused with anything else.

Apart from the differences in the frequency and quality of their ultrasonic signals, other characteristics distinguish the horseshoes from the whisperers. At close quarters the horseshoes will be seen to lack the narrow pointed inner ear, or tragus, which is so characteristic of the latter. Also the horseshoes wrap their wings around their bodies in true Count Dracula style, rather than holding them at the sides like the other bats.

Distinguishing between the two species of horseshoe is not difficult either. As already mentioned, the pulses are at different frequencies. There is also the size difference. In flight the wingspan of the Greater is close to that of the Noctule, being about 325mm (13in); the Lesser, on the other hand, only attains about 210mm (8½in). At rest the size difference is just as obvious. The Lesser Horseshoe is a small bat with a body length of about 50mm (2in) about half the size of the Greater. The flight style is also a means of differentiation; the Greater has a relatively slow moth-like wing beat, while the Lesser's wings appear almost a blur as it negotiates the obstacles in the caves and barns where it lives.

Both species of horseshoe, in common with other bats, have different summer and winter quarters. They use buildings during the breeding season and caves for winter hibernation. Unfortunately bats which share buildings with humans are particularly prone to disturbance and destruction, and a recent threat is the widespread use of pesticides and other wood preservatives. Bats pick up these lethal chemicals by contact with the treated wood and death results within a day or two. A more lingering death results from taking in small amounts of the poison with their prey, or by breathing in the atmosphere which is saturated by the chemicals. The latter are extremely persistent and far outlast the thirty-year guarantee which accompanies their application; they are a threat to the survival not only of this year's bats, but of all bats using that roost for many years to come. It is fairly typical of man that he should destroy his allies in the fight against insect 'pests'.

Horseshoe bats are also particularly at risk during their winter hibernation, though this is a dangerous time for all bats. During hibernation a profound change takes place within the bat's metabolism, and all its bodily functions slow down to such an extent as to be hardly noticeable. Any disturbance which leads to awakening and activity will result in the bat having to replace some of the valuable food reserves which it has built up to last it through to spring. It takes to flight to catch insects, thus more energy is expended, and the whole business of waking and flying becomes a vicious circle. All too often there are no insects to find and so the bat expends even more energy in its searches. But without the replacement of these reserves to see it through the winter, the bat will surely die. Horseshoe bats, being light sleepers, are very prone to such disturbance, and it seems highly likely that this has been a major factor in their decline. The Greater Horseshoe Bat has been reduced in numbers by a staggering 98 per cent over the last century.

If, therefore, you come across horseshoe bats in their winter roost or hibernaculum, take great care and, if possible, make a detour around them. Cigarette smoke offends their nostrils and they are extremely quick to feel any vibration. But more than anything it is strong torchlight which they detest. A torch beam will make them curl up almost as if in pain and waking up nearly always follows, resulting in flight to a more secluded, but perhaps less suitable, location. Under no circumstances should you stand looking at any bat with a strong torch.

Conservation

It is indeed sad, almost an indictment on the human race, to see harmless wildlife like bats come perilously near to extinction. Even the so-called 'common' bats have been reduced by up to 50 per cent over the last few years. There is little doubt that man is largely to blame; not least because of the superstition and ignorance with which he surrounds them. On a recent visit to a threatened bat roost, I was appalled when the operator for a large wood-treatment company related with glee how he used to catch bats. He had two methods – the first was a quick spray with insecticide, which stopped the bats dead in their tracks; the second, less subtle, was to use a tennis racket.

Bats are not something to get rid of, their feeding preferences make them a positive benefit. They do not bite unless handled roughly, they certainly do not suck blood and they carry no diseases dangerous to man. Their droppings do not smell except when a roof leaks and they get wet. In fact the dry, friable pellets produced by bats have been suggested as an addition to roof insulation or as garden fertiliser. Having bats as lodgers is something of an honour; it is not everyone who gets the opportunity to study these animals at close quarters.

Once householders are converted to bats they often become intensely interested and make regular records such as the time at which bats emerge especially with reference to weather conditions, when the bats first arrive in spring or summer and when they leave for the winter. Even for the common bats, such information is sadly lacking. If carried out, year after year, a great deal can be learned about how individual colonies are faring. It is such information, collected largely by amateurs, which has highlighted the dramatic drop in bat numbers over the years. Every bat enthusiast could do much worse than enlist the help of friends in telling him where the bats are and in keeping counts of their numbers.

The combined effects of loss of roosts, disturbance during hibernation and intake of chemicals from roof timbers (both mentioned in the section on horseshoe bats), must amplify any natural threats such as adverse weather during the critical breeding season. But other factors, as yet not fully understood, may be important too. For instance, site preferences within a cave are still little understood; some bats position themselves in the most exposed parts when other sites within only a few feet seem far more suitable to us. Air currents, temperature fluctuations, absence of light and the presence of footholds must all play their part in the bats' choice and are perhaps critical for survival. Different species may choose the same cave as a roost, and occasionally they are found in close proximity; but more often they roost apart. Some secrete themselves in narrow cracks, others suspend themselves from the cave roof. This is just one facet of bat behaviour which needs careful study.

Thankfully, over the last few years the interest in bats has increased and, hopefully, legislation in the form of the Wildlife and Countryside Act (1981), which protects all bats, has not come too late. It is now illegal to kill, capture or disturb any bat of any species and those who wish to handle bats while carrying out serious study have to obtain a licence from the Nature Conservancy Council. All naturalists should become familiar with the Act, ensure they follow it to the letter, and set an example to others less familiar with the problems our animals face.

Bats are not the easiest group to study but, as already stressed, the amateur has a valuable part to play. And if, when you are trying to identify a bat, all you get is a glimpse as it flits away between the branches of a tree, do not give up. The chances are that the bat will be back, if not later the same evening, probably the next – bats tend to be very regular in their habits. And you do not need to work alone, for there are bat enthusiasts in every county and local 'Bat Groups' have been set up to give advice and encouragement. For further information contact The Institute of Terrestrial Ecology, Monk's Wood Experimental Station, Abbots Ripton, Huntingdon PE17 2LS. Remember, every scrap of information is another step on the road to the full understanding and conservation of these delightful creatures.

9 CONDUCT, EQUIPMENT AND CLOTHING

Like all hobbies, nature watching has its rules and regulations. Sometimes these may appear to be a nuisance but they are always there for a good reason, whether to safeguard humans or the animals themselves. Perhaps the most important Act of Parliament in recent years as far as wildlife is concerned is the Wildlife and Countryside Act (1981). This Act is very broad in its scope and may in some parts leave a little to be desired. As an Act of Parliament, however, it must be obeyed, firstly because it is the law and secondly because it is an attempt to safeguard, amongst other things, the wildlife which we all enjoy. Certain animals not previously afforded any protection are now included in the various schedules of this Act. Such protection may include banning of animal capture, disturbance and photography. It is essential that any naturalist becomes thoroughly acquainted with the relevant sections of this Act and copies can be found in local libraries, museums, or council offices. If you have any difficulty in obtaining one you can order it through a good bookseller.

Special legislation may apply locally in the form of Bird Sanctuary orders or other areas of special protection, so it is always worth finding out what is going on in your area. Most land is owned by someone and it is only common courtesy to ask for permission before you go walking across a farmer's fields or into someone's wood. Furtive rambles into the countryside might seem perfectly normal but remember that torches, camouflaged clothing and night mean only one thing to landowners – poachers. I have found that most farmers and gamekeepers are more than happy to let you on to their land if you explain what you want to do and when you are doing it. They will also be able to tell you what is going on, where to look and what to look for. They will also be interested in what you have seen.

Nature reserves can often show something special and are a good example of a habitat. From time to time you may wish to visit one for a particular study and you should always inform whoever is in charge what you are doing. The chances are that you will be welcomed with open arms since any information you gain could be of use to the management. Experiments are always going on in nature reserves and you should make sure you do not interfere with them, either by blundering into a special area or by setting up your own experiment in opposition.

At all times remember that you are a guest of landowner and nature itself, and only by showing consideration and respect will you get the most out of your hobby. Always leave the countryside as you found it.

Field Notebook and its Use

Perhaps the single most important item you take into the field with you is a field notebook. There are times when the taking of notes seems pointless and tiresome, but apart from giving a permanent record of your nocturnal wanderings, it will encourage you to adopt a methodical approach. The field notebook acts as an extension of your memory which, no matter how reliable you think it is, will let you down eventually so that you just cannot remember which bat it was you saw, or on what plant that moth was laying its eggs. Working in a museum I am constantly referring to other people's notebooks for past distribution records and some leave a lot to be desired. But if your field notes are thorough, the notebook will provide an invaluable source of reference throughout your lifetime and be of immense importance to future generations of naturalists.

Field notebooks come in a variety of shapes and sizes, and although the final choice is a personal one, there are some

Fig 30 The field notebook is the most important piece of equipment you will take with you and should contain as much information as possible

points which you should bear in mind. A hardback notebook with waterproof cover is ideal, but at least make sure the binding is not coloured by a dye which will run when wet. The hard cover provides a sturdy surface on which to write, and helps to prevent the pages from dog-earing. The way the book opens is really immaterial, but those that open up and over, away from you, have less area to glare in torchlight and to get wet. A piece of elastic to hold back the pages and some means of securing a pencil are also advantageous.

Your method of entering information is again a personal choice, but you should aim for a standard format which will facilitate later reference and dictate to you at time of entry the basic information required. The name of the site, with clear indication of where it lies, is essential. You know where the site is, but others using your book may not. Remember that local names for places are not always the same as those on published maps, and use the latter where it is given. The name of the nearest town or village and any landmarks are useful in pinpointing your site as are map coordinates either as mileages east or west etc of a landmark or, preferably, as a full grid reference. For example, Haytor Rocks SX758770, 1 mile east of Haytor Vale, 2½ miles south of Manaton, should enable anyone to find the locality in question. The method of arriving at grid references is usually given at the bottom of all maps produced by the Ordnance Survey, but basically you start with the number of the vertical line on the left of the site and estimate at how many tenths of the total distance to the next line on the right the site is – the numbers of the lines are given at the map edges. Next you start at the line immediately below the site and work upwards to the next line doing the same estimation. The two sets of figures you end up with are known as the eastings and northings and provide your point of reference. The grid letters – SX in the example opposite – identify the 100 kilometre square within which you are working and can usually be found at the bottom of the map.

Details of the site itself might include a sketch map of the route you take, any fences, ditches or walls that have to be negotiated in the dark, and any other relevant features such as ponds, clearings, patches of particular tree species and habitat types. Details of ownership and any entry restrictions are also useful. On arrival at the site, a few minutes spent noting weather conditions such as cloud cover, wind direction and temperature will provide a framework for the more detailed observations you make later and will help you to interpret

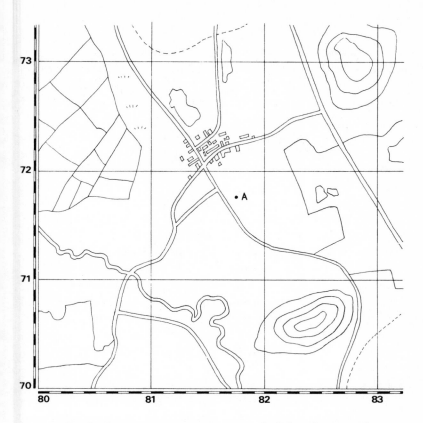

Fig 31   Grid references are an accurate method of identifying a point on a map; to obtain the grid reference take the following example as a guide. First of all the easting position is determined. Take the western edge of the square in which the point lies (the grid line number will be found at the bottom or top of the map), ie 81. Then estimate the position of the point in tenths of a square from this line, ie approximately 8/10ths. The easting is thus 818. To obtain the northing the same principle is followed working up from the base of the square to obtain 718. The full six-figure grid reference is thus 818718. With the addition of the grid letters signifying which map you are using a unique position within the UK will be found

those observations in a more meaningful way.

The fullest information will, of course, be that directly concerned with the animals observed, and this should be entered at or immediately following your sightings. Species, sexes present, numbers, and good descriptions of what the animals or birds were doing is essential. Impressions and thoughts should be entered as they occur and are still fresh;

even the most ridiculous interpretations will conjure up a scene and enable you to formulate a more plausible explanation in the cold light of day. Liberal use of annotated sketch maps and drawings is a good habit to get into, as they will all jar something in your memory.

It is always very tempting to use abbreviations, particularly when you would rather be watching something than writing about it. If you do use them, make sure you provide yourself with a key as soon as possible after you have written them down. For instance, 22.04 $\male$ sniff look $\male$ 22.05 scratch → E. r.f. N.23.22 does not mean much by itself, but with a key to the symbols it means: 'At four minutes past ten the first badger came half out of the sett, sniffed the air and looked around. After one minute it emerged completely, had a scratch, and moved off towards the east. It returned from the north at twenty-two minutes past eleven.' Timing should always be noted using the 24-hour clock or, if you insist, carefully add am or pm as necessary – there are times of year when 7 o'clock is always during the hours of darkness!

Clothing
The first consideration when out in the field is the welfare of the animals themselves, the second is your own well-being. The weather is often inclement and your enjoyment and powers of observation will both be impaired if you are in the slightest way uncomfortable. Footwear should provide protection from cold rough ground as well as being waterproof and easy to wear. Wellington boots are suitable in most conditions, but they can cause problems – I have lost count of the number of times I have left one behind in thick mud when it should have been on my foot. Certainly they should be avoided if you need to climb rocks or negotiate fallen trees, for then they can prove awkward and dangerous. Good strong climbing or walking boots or shoes present a much safer alternative.

Jackets and trousers should be light in weight, waterproof and both warm in winter and cool in summer. They also need to be tough enough to deflect the inevitable brambles and barbed wire. No clothing incorporates all these things, but the nearest jackets are the wax-covered ones much favoured by bird watchers and other country lovers. These are expensive, but are well worth the money. All clothing should fit snugly but not be restrictive; on the other hand jackets should not be so loose as to flap in the breeze nor should any clothing have shiny buttons or clanking buckles — all these are guaranteed to scare away most animals. The very popular and lightweight nylon clothing is very unsuitable for most nocturnal activities due to the constant rustling which accompanies your every breath and movement. Dark coloured clothing is definitely recommended, as it helps you to blend with your surroundings. It is tempting to buy jackets and trousers with a multitude of useful looking pockets, but beware; while a few pockets are useful, a lot merely provide hiding places for all your paraphernalia.

Perhaps the best way to obtain your 'naturalist's uniform' is to visit an army surplus store. After all the military have spent a great deal of time and money in developing this type of clothing for similar reasons of concealment and comfort, although with a different stimulus.

Binoculars

Although primarily designed for daytime use, binoculars can also prove a boon to the nocturnal observer. Modern lens technology has produced a wide variety of models which will function at low light levels; obviously they will not help you when there is no light at all, but the illumination from the moon or from a red-filtered torch is usually quite sufficient for most purposes.

Lightness is of paramount importance, especially when you are carrying other equipment with you, and so your binoculars should not be large and heavy. Those favoured by bird watchers are ideal. But you should always try them out, at least in the street, before you buy, and a sympathetic dealer or friend may let you borrow a pair to try at night.

Hand Lens

A hand lens is an indispensable piece of equipment for any naturalist. Readily available from dealers and many opticians, they come in bewildering varieties; but a sturdy lens with metal casing is essential. A useful magnification would be about 10× and the actual optics should be achromatic to prevent distortion. Hand lenses are probably the easiest items of equipment to lose and although initially not expensive, constant replacements will become a burden on your purse. Add to this their habit of hiding in the corners of pockets and it becomes expedient to attach them to your person in some way. A piece of strong cord to hang the lens around the neck is favoured by some people, but this always seems to get in the way and I prefer to tie the lens on a length of cord and attach this to a buttonhole or belt.

Compass and Whistle

A small compass is a good idea not only for taking bearings on the direction of the wind or the direction in which an animal moves, but also to help you to find your way home if you get lost. While on the subject of getting lost, or even suffering some sort of injury preventing you from moving, a whistle is a good means of attracting attention.

Specimen Tubes and Boxes

A small selection of specimen tubes is always useful to a naturalist. Whether you are making detailed studies of invertebrates, or merely collecting samples of the food or the droppings of vertebrates, containers will ensure that items are kept separate and will also provide better protection against damage than simply placing the specimens in your pocket or the bottom of the rucksack.

Circular cardboard boxes and glass lids are made for lepidopterists – moths readily fly towards the glass where there is light and thus make capture more simple; these containers are of course suitable for many other invertebrates as well. Glass tubes with polythene stoppers are a cheap type of container, but they do have the disadvantage of being breakable – a fault which tends not to occur with plastic tubes. The latter however are prone to become cloudy after being used a few times. On balance the glass type is preferable and, with a little care, breakages can be kept to a minimum. If you

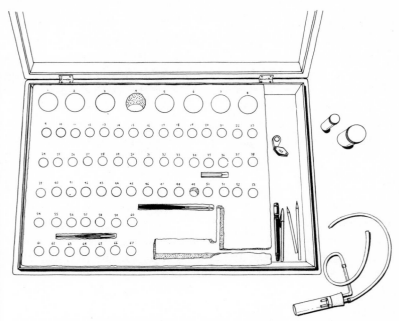

Fig 32   Having a place for everything and everything in its place should be the maxim of all naturalists; a converted butterfly store box makes an ideal and easily carried container for small or fragile pieces of equipment

are going to collect invertebrates in any numbers for study, some form of container to protect the tubes is essential. I use a modified butterfly storebox into which expanded polystyrene ceiling tiles, with holes bored in them to hold the tubes firmly, have been stuck. Other holes and grooves provide safe anchorage for forceps, camel-hair brush and other small pieces of equipment. A notebook and pencil can be attached inside the lid, and the whole thing can be fitted with a shoulder strap for easy carrying.

Torches
A good source of light is essential to illuminate the objects of nocturnal scrutiny and to help you negotiate the hazards encountered during after-dark expeditions. The power of the torch depends very much on what you are observing; for close work a relatively small pocket torch will normally suffice, a more powerful torch will obviously be necessary if you are studying a badger sett from a distance. Usually a diffused light

is the most useful, but there will be occasions when a narrow beam will serve your purposes better. Battery life is perhaps the most important consideration, and great care should be exercised so as not to run out of power at a critical moment in your observations or when you are about to try and find your way back out of a dark wood.

Modern batteries, particularly the longlife alkali type, are quite good; but even so a set of spares in your pocket is a good idea. The ideal solution is to buy a torch that will take rechargeable batteries. There are many torches on the market which run off a wet cell or, if you are reasonably handy with electricity, you should be able to construct such a light from a small motorcycle battery and parts available from the nearest breaker's yard. Modern nickel-cadmium cells are now available for most sizes of torch, although they are expensive and need a special type of charger – but at least you can be sure of going into the field with a fully charged torch.

Hand-held torches are cheapest and in many ways provide an all-purpose light source. Some of them have the reflector at right angles to the main body, and can be clipped to the belt thus leaving both hands free. A wide range of torches which can be worn on the forehead are also available; these are very useful and can be as cheap as a few pounds, and are available from caving or mountaineering suppliers.

Many animals are shy of bright light, but are relatively insensitive to red light, and thus some means of attaching a red filter to the reflector is essential. If the filter is hinged to the latter it can be moved in front of, or away from, the light as you desire or circumstances dictate.

It is useful to gather together a variety of torches to cover all eventualities – you will soon gain enough experience to be able to choose the most suitable one for the job in hand. But a reliable, general-purpose torch should always be taken.

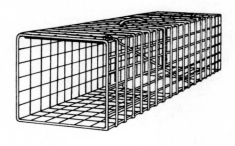

10 BAITS, LURES AND TRAPS

There is no doubt that more than half the fun of natural history is coming across the unexpected. Chance encounters are always a thrill, and indeed form the basis of your knowledge and the foundations of more scientific study. As time passes, however, you may wish to make an in-depth study of a particular animal or group of animals. Identification of some of the larger animals can, however, be difficult at a distance; and when it comes to the smaller invertebrates identification is only possible by obtaining specimens for study under a microscope. If more serious study is planned, you will have to adopt a more methodical approach than that of the casual observer. For instance, population, home range and distribution studies are all enhanced by knowing how many of a particular group or species is in a particular area at a given time, and you may well have to capture specimens to obtain this information. Photographic and sound recording are both facilitated if you can expect an animal to be in a given place at a given time, thus enabling you to set up your equipment beforehand to obtain the best results. The use of baits is a well-tried technique for attracting animals to a particular place; if necessary traps can also be utilised to capture the subjects of your study.

Baiting normally consists of laying out a supply of attractive food for the animal concerned and, properly done, virtually guarantees a visitation at a particular place. Indeed some small mammals become so accustomed to an easy source of food that they appear night after night and may even keep to a rigid

Fig 33 Regular baiting at the same place will attract many types of animals; the addition of a red-filtered lamp above the point will greatly aid observation and photography

schedule. Whilst this sort of activity is obviously very convenient for the observer it may prove detrimental to the individual animal concerned. Firstly, if an animal becomes accustomed to an attractive though unnatural food source its health may suffer — rather like children and sweets. Secondly, easy food sources can make some animals lazy and, if the supply is suddenly withdrawn, they may starve, having become too dependent on the rations you supply. Baiting as an aid to your studies thus burdens you with responsibilities and, as always, you should first and foremost consider the animal's welfare. Baiting should use as natural a food as possible, and should only be carried out in the same spot for short periods at a time.

Assembling

Scent plays a very important part in communication between insects, not least as a sexual attractant. The production of scent or pheromones by a female moth enables a male to find her even when she is apparently concealed beneath vegetation or unable to advertise her presence by flight because she is wingless (see page 67). The scent is produced from special glands towards the end of her abdomen; these she is able to expose at will by extending the latter's posterior segments and uncovering the membranes. The scent itself can be extremely powerful and experiments have shown that only small quantities, as little as $\frac{1}{10,000}$ million millionth of a gram, are necessary to produce a positive reaction in a male of the same species. Such females, or even the extracted scents from their abdomens, have been used extensively by collectors, and have even produced an economic spin-off as a bait for the males of certain pest species.

Attracting moths by this method is known as 'assembling'. A virgin female of the species — to be certain the female is a virgin it is perhaps best to obtain a freshly pupated specimen — is held in one place and allowed to 'call' by producing scent. (You will need to collect a number of pupae, keep them separate and watch them in order to be sure of obtaining a female.) The simplest method is to place her in a muslin bag suspended above the ground. If the males are to be collected,

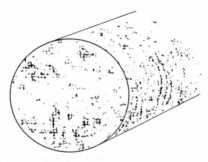

WIND DIRECTION

PLASTIC FUNNEL

VIRGIN FEMALE
CALLING

MALE MOTHS FLY
UPWIND TO
CALLING FEMALE

8" (203 mm)

1½" (38·5)

PHEROMONES CARRIED ON
WIND TO AWAITING MALES

Fig 34   Many female moths attract males by means of scents (pheromones) – if a female is placed in an assembler the males will arrive from great distances and be captured for close study; an assembler can be easily made from a wire frame covered in muslin with a funnel at one end to allow entry of the males

some form of trap will be necessary allowing the males to enter but not escape. A simple, very light one can be constructed from old wire coathangers, a muslin cylinder and a funnel, and the female is placed in this and the whole apparatus suspended. About 2m (6ft) above the ground is usually suffi-cient, but you can experiment with different heights in different localities. The funnel end should be orientated away from the wind direction so that an airstream passes over the female and out through it. The scent is then carried downwind and will be received by any males 'en route', which will then fly upwind towards the source of the scent, ie the female, and congregate in large numbers. These males perceive the scent from considerable distances, often a mile or more, and even competing smells, say from built-up areas, do not impair their efficiency. Some moths though are more reliant on pheromones as an attractive agent than others, and as a general rule those species in which the male has feathery antennae are best for this purpose, these antennae being the organs of perception that 'smell' the scents produced by the female. The eggars are among the best moths to start with as they seem to be particularly good at finding females by this method of attraction. Certain weather conditions can enhance or limit the carrying power of the scents. The best nights are when it is humid and warm with a light breeze to carry the scent to the males. A distinct drawback of this method of attracting moths is that it only attracts one species, and then only males.

Light

The attractiveness of light to many insects, and in particular the night-flying moths, has long been taken advantage of by collectors as a means of gathering them into one place for capture or study. A light by an open window on any summer evening will attract a great many varieties, telling you much about the nocturnal insect fauna of the immediate neighbourhood. Even in the centre of a town you can soon create a timetable of visitors as they chop and change throughout the night. Street lamps also attract insects and you could do worse than walk down your road noting different visitors. It will soon become obvious, however, that all the lights in a given area such as a group of houses are in competition with each other, and consequently the 'haul' is diluted. Taking a light source out into the countryside not only overcomes this problem, but also enables you to sample different habitats and to experiment with different types of light. A bright moonlit night will, however, reduce your success rate. There are many designs of attracting equipment using light, ranging from a simple bulb to sophisticated apparatus that not only attracts the insects but also captures them, thus leaving you free to pursue other avenues of investigation. Perhaps the easiest method is to run an extension cable from the house mains supply out into adjoining fields, or even to the bottom of your garden if other light sources are not too near. Fully waterproof leads are essential for this, and you should have a word with your friendly electrician who will no doubt be able to advise you. More freedom, through less reliance on a mains source, is gained by using a portable light. At its simplest, a hand torch or other small light source such as a camping-gas or Tilley lamp will prove very convenient and, up to a point, effective. If you decide to use some of the more powerful electrical equipment, a portable power source such as a car battery or a small generator will be necessary. Car headlights are an obviously transportable light source and will prove very effective, but they do have the limitation of normally being restricted to roadside use.

Although a light on its own is sufficient to attract many insects, its efficiency can be greatly improved by the simple expedient of shining it onto a white surface. An old white sheet is very good for this and, as well as being easy to carry, can be draped in almost any situation, such as over a convenient gate or fence, or suspended from a tree. When a sheet is used, the best results will be gained if it can be draped to provide both vertical and horizontal surfaces, thus catering for the vagaries of the resting orientation of moths.

The content of the light source is of importance in determining which insects are attracted and which are not. A considerable amount of research has gone into this question and results show that the most effective sources are those which transmit light within the ultra-violet end of the spectrum. Most commercially available lights for attracting insects are based on the mercury-vapour lamp. Some use light that is so far into the ultra violet as to be virtually invisible to the human eye, and these are the most effective.

Light Traps

Having attracted the insects it is often useful to trap them for closer study or even collecting; a light trap fulfils this need and can be left unattended if necessary. The trap consists of a light source, normally ultra-violet or mercury vapour, and a box to collect the insects in. The light is suspended above the box which normally has four radiating veins made of a transparent material such as perspex to interrupt the flight of the insects as they circle the light. The insects blunder into the veins and fall

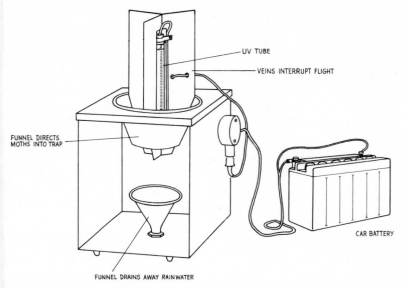

UV TUBE

VEINS INTERRUPT FLIGHT

FUNNEL DIRECTS
MOTHS INTO TRAP

CAR BATTERY

FUNNEL DRAINS AWAY RAINWATER

Fig 35   The Heath light trap is portable and effective; the ultra-violet light is especially attractive to many species of moths as well as a host of other insects

through a funnel into the box. The box itself contains cardboard egg cartons loosely packed to provide hiding places for the moths.

Sugaring

Sugaring is a method of attraction which, like assembling, takes full advantage of the acute sense of smell possessed by many insects. Partiality to sweet smells is a feature of such fliers, flowers being perhaps the best known natural example, their aroma acting as a lure to insects which are rewarded with nectar for their pollination of the blooms. Providing a concentration of sweet substances artificially is one of the simplest and most effective means of attracting a wide variety of insects, in large numbers, into a small area. A basic mixture can be purchased from entomological dealers, but it is so simple to make that you might as well do it yourself, varying the ingredients with experience and habitat to gain maximum efficiency. A thick treacly substance like molasses forms the base of the mixture; to this is added twice the weight of sugar and a little stale beer. The mixture is then gently boiled to give it thickness. Care should be taken to ensure that the mixture is of the correct consistency, ie thick enough to adhere to the brush which you use to apply it, but not so thick that it cannot be easily worked. Just before application a small quantity of rum or amylacetate should be added; this will give a soporific effect and inhibit flight as you approach, thus making observation easier. Different flavourings may produce variation in the species attracted to the mixture, and should be tried. The equipment necessary for sugaring apart from the mixture itself is very simple – a container for carrying the mixture, a brush to apply it and a light source to illuminate the 'catch', are all you need.

Sugaring will pay dividends in almost any locality, from open moorland to a clearing in a dense wood. As a general rule thick vegetation will not provide good results, and any sweet-smelling natural competition should be avoided as nature has already furnished the lure for you. Sugaring stations should be established, because a spot which is repeatedly sugared is always more attractive than a fresh one. As with any

Fig 36   Sugaring patches are best applied to each of a row of trees and will attract many types of invertebrates

method of attracting insects by smell, weather conditions are very important and careful note should be kept of wind direction, cloud cover etc. Heavy breezes, unseasonal cold spells and very dry nights will all have a detrimental effect on your attempts to attract insects; as with the assembling, humidity with a gentle breeze and a certain amount of cloud cover is best. Bats know better than we do which are good insect nights and good insect districts, and their presence or absence will provide a clue as to where and when you will be most successful. The best time for sugaring is just before dusk, but not too early or its effect will be lost on the relatively barren air of the day. Insects fly at different times of night and thus you should not be keen to get home because of apparent early failure.

Other Attractants

It is not only sweet-smelling substances which prove attractive to insects and by a little observation you will soon find a multitude of 'baits' some of which may prove to be very specific. Water in the form of puddles, for instance, is always worth watching for the many insects which visit it. The dung of animals and even their carcases are irresistible targets for all sorts of animals.

Pitfall Traps

A pitfall trap is essentially a container set into the ground into which animals fall whilst going about their daily activities. There is nothing sophisticated about it and a 450g (1lb) jamjar is perfectly good for most purposes. The jar is set into the ground so that its lip is flush with the surface, and any animal falling into it is prevented from escaping by being unable to gain purchase on the jar's smooth sides. Clearly an open jar set into the ground will collect water if it starts to rain, so it is a good idea to provide some sort of roof to prevent this from happening. A piece of slate propped up on four pebbles and weighted down with a rock normally does the trick.

Pitfall traps will catch most of the smaller ground fauna, including small mammals such as mice, shrews and voles as

PEBBLES RAISE SLATE AND ALLOW ENTRY

SLATE ROOF PREVENTS RAIN ENTERING AND MAMMALS ESCAPING

LARGE JAR SHOULD BE DEEP ENOUGH FOR MOST SMALL MAMMALS

BEDDING MATERIAL KEEPS MAMMAL WARM AND DRY

SUITABLE BAIT ATTRACTS MAMMAL AND ALSO PROVIDES FOOD DURING PERIOD OF CAPTURE

Fig 37 A pitfall trap is a cheap and easy-to-make piece of equipment which if used properly does not cause captives any distress

well as many kinds of invertebrates. When setting them for small mammals they should be dry and have no vegetation protruding which could facilitate escape. If invertebrates are your target, a killing and preserving agent is desirable otherwise some members of the catch will eat others; it is also a good idea to lower the slate roof so as to leave a space large enough for these animals to get in but too small to allow entry of mammals. Many preservatives have been used, but one of the most satisfactory and easiest to obtain is ethylene glycol. This chemical is commonly available as antifreeze, but remember to buy the colourless type otherwise you will end up with a collection of nicely dyed specimens.

When trapping for invertebrates you will only have to visit the traps infrequently as the preservative will keep the contents in good condition. If, on the other hand, you are trapping for vertebrates, you will have to make regular inspections – say every couple of hours – because your catch will soon die of starvation or exposure. With pitfall traps you should always be prepared for the unexpected; it is not uncommon to find a frog in the trap when you were expecting mice or spiders.

Box and Cage Traps

Most box and cage traps work on a fairly simple principle of a trip mechanism which releases a door once the animal has entered the trap, and thus captures it. Many types have been developed, and a visit to a large hardware store or farm suppliers will show the variety available. Cage traps tend to be used for the larger mammals; having been perfected for use in the study and control of pest species such as mink, coypu, rats etc, they can of course, if suitably baited, be used for many other mammal species. The smaller mammals such as shrews, voles and mice can be captured by pitfall traps as already described, but the use of box traps allows for greater selectivity and is safer for the animals themselves.

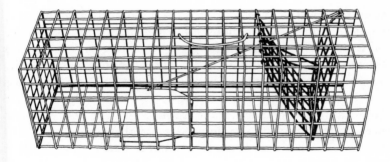

Fig 38   Cage traps can be purchased from agricultural suppliers and are used for trapping larger mammals such as rats, stoats, mink etc; they have an advantage over other traps in that you can see what you have caught before you open the trap

The Longworth is the type of box trap often used by field workers; essentially it consists of two aluminium boxes one of which, the entrance tunnel, fits into a larger one, the nest box. Bait is placed in the nest box to attract the small mammal concerned; the mammal enters the tunnel in search of the bait and, as it does so, the trip-wire is depressed, the door released and the animal captured. The nest box should always be well

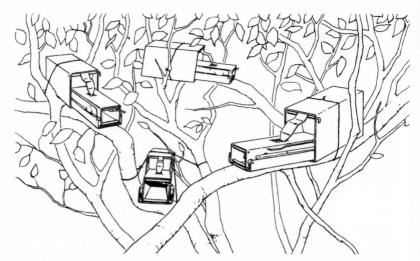

Fig 39 Longworth traps set at various heights above ground level will help to establish the vertical distribution of small mammals

supplied with food and warm dry nesting material in order to prevent death from starvation or exposure before you make your next visit. This trap is quite a sophisticated piece of equipment and, by judicious adjustment of a wire spring, the pressure necessary for releasing the door can be varied, thus providing a very simple method of selecting mammals by weight. However, you do have to pay for sophistication and the Longworth is quite expensive, especially when used in large numbers for population studies, and the cost starts to become frightening. Simple versions of these traps can easily be manufactured out of readily available materials and, while they may not be as effective or indeed have such a long life, they are considerably cheaper. I have found a very simple method of producing traps with no more than lengths of square-section PVC drainpipe, bent wire coathangers and a few screws. With these simple materials quite intricate trip and locking mechanisms can be produced.

Setting Traps

The welfare of the animals themselves is the first thing to be considered when setting traps. They should not be set in such a way as to injure or maim; and if you are not sure that you can visit the traps regularly, every couple of hours or so, the traps should be removed to prevent unnecessary death through your negligence. Even in the space of two hours some mammals can suffer starvation, and this is particularly true of shrews – active little creatures which spend most of their waking hours either eating or searching for food. As already mentioned, there should be plenty of food in the trap, and nesting material in the form of a handful of dry grasses or even shredded newspaper.

The actual positioning of the traps will vary with the locality and the animals themselves. Many small mammals always move along the same route, and these are obviously good places to set traps. Animals often take natural short-cuts, for example a branch leading down a steep bank, and these are also excellent sites. Bait by itself will often attract animals to leave their normal routes, and when first setting a series of traps in an area it may prove most useful to prebait first. Laying bait of the type you are going to use either on the bare ground, or actually in the trap itself but with the door jammed open, is a good way of introducing the animals to their new food source and is practised by many professional naturalists.

The type of bait to be used obviously varies with the animal you wish to capture and experience will tell you which is the best. Knowing what the animal eats in the wild state is obviously helpful and more detail of food will be found in the section of the book concerned with the animals themselves. You must remember that whatever bait you use will be in competition with such natural foods and the animals may prefer to find it in more familiar places. It may therefore be more productive to limit your trapping to those times of the year when natural food is at a premium or to offer a totally artificial supply which is more attractive to the animals than their normal food. Oats are a very good standby for many of the small mammals and even shrews are attracted by crushed raisins. I have found the most successful bait for the small mammals to be broken chocolate and raisin biscuits; however this is not a very healthy food and should be used in small quantities as an attractant only, the food supply for the sustenance of the mammal while trapped should be far more like its natural food.

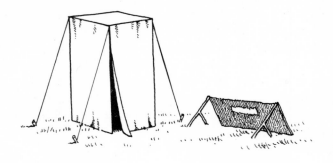

11   BUILDING AND PLACING HIDES

Eventually, as your enthusiasm grows, it will be necessary to spend longer periods of time in one place, perhaps making detailed photographic and sound recordings of a particular animal. In such a situation concealment from the target, protection of delicate equipment from the elements and your own comfort will be of the upmost importance; the erection of a hide is probably the best method of satisfying all these criteria. A hide can be very simple and take the form of a handy rock, tree or wall behind which to secrete yourself. Even a car can provide the necessary screening, so long as it is in a position where the subject expects it to be – say in a layby or car park – or can be accustomed to seeing it. Many animals get quite oblivious to the presence of cars if you take care.

Often, however, you will find yourself in an area where cover is lacking and then you will have to provide your own. A screen made from branches and other vegetation lashed together with strong string is easily constructed, and will serve admirably; but for longer periods of a few days a more permanent structure is necessary to protect you and your equipment from the weather. Birdwatchers have long realised the value of hides, and many of the commercially available models have been designed with their needs in mind. They can be purchased from natural-history suppliers, but the design is so basic that it is easy for the handyperson to build one. Alternatively, a standard camping latrine tent can be converted.

Fig 40 A small screen of canvas and vegetation is easy to carry and can be of considerable help in concealing you from your quarry

Building a Hide

Constructing a hide is not difficult and has the advantage that, as you build, you can alter the plan to suit your own requirements. The basic hide consists of a framework, about 1.5m (5ft) high and about 1m (3ft) square, which supports a canvas covering coloured to blend with the surroundings in which it is to be used. The framework can be constructed of any material strong enough to support itself and the covering, but light enough to be carried in often difficult conditions. Wood is preferred by some naturalists, but has the disadvantages of being heavy and prone to warping; some form of light metal tubing is probably better – metal telescopic tent poles are probably best of all. Using the dimensions already given, the four poles which form the uprights should be filed, sawn or hammered to a point at one end to allow them to be easily pushed into the ground to give some rigidity to the structure. The four poles for the top of the frame should have their ends bent at right angles and hammered to fit into the tops of the uprights. The next stage is the covering of canvas, hessian or other material. Waterproofed material should be avoided, as it can be very noisy when exposed to the lightest of showers. Polythene sheeting, or for the really sophisticated, a waterproof tent can be added inside to give protection from the weather. Four pieces of fabric are needed for the sides of the hide and one piece for the roof. These are sewn together to form a rectangular box open at one end and down one edge –

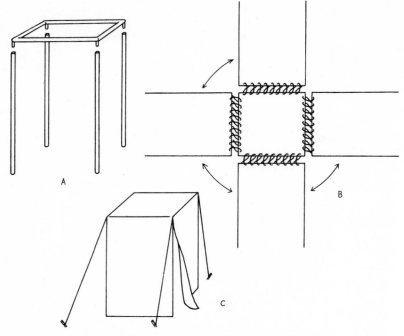

Fig 41 A more permanent hide; easily built from tent poles and canvas, they provide concealment and comfort

this open edge forming the entrance. Buttons or lacing are then added to this edge as a means of closure; zip fasteners may seem easier, but should be avoided due to their noisiness and their habit of jamming. When erected the covering should be a tight fit, and its lower edge will need to be secured to the ground to prevent noisy flapping of the material; tent pegs are ideal for this. The hide on its own is inherently unstable, and guy ropes have to be attached to each corner and secured to the ground.

Inside the Hide
Having constructed the hide, the next step is to cut peepholes, the positions of which will vary with the situation and the animals being watched. You should always be prepared to cut new holes on site, but one in the front and one in each of the sides is a good start. For each hole cut three sides of a square to provide a flap which opens down away from you, these can be laced to enable closure when not in use. The peepholes should

be at a comfortable height for the observer and it is a good idea
to cut them while sitting on the stool to be used during your
watching. Inevitably some equipment will accompany you
into the hide, and if hooks are provided the job of finding it
when working in very dark conditions will be made a great
deal easier.

Comfort is essential; prolonged periods sitting in one place
will lead to you getting cold, so that warm clothing is highly
recommended. It is essential, too, that the stool you sit on is
comfortable. A folding camping stool is very good, but it is
advisable to fix it to the ground with tent pegs to prevent it
from toppling over. Finally, survival rations should be taken
into the hide to sustain you through the night – food and a hot
drink will do much to raise flagging spirits resulting from lack

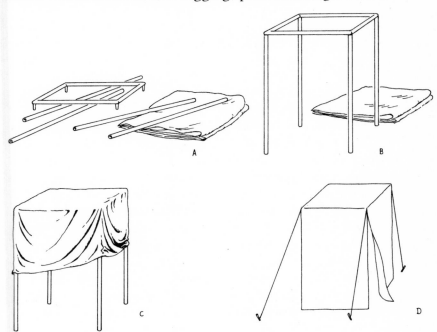

Fig 42   Hides can be put in position by moving them nearer to the chosen
spot each day; another method is to gradually construct the hide on site
thus giving animals a chance to get used to it. Both methods should cause
as little disturbance as possible; observation should cease if there is any sign
of stress on the part of the subject

of participation by the subjects of your observations. Noisy wrappings on sandwiches should be avoided as they can produce enough sound to alarm and cause animals to flee; tissue paper or kitchen towels should be used instead of greaseproof paper or foil.

Positioning the Hide

There is no standard position for a hide to suit every occasion; every site must be assessed to find the best place. There will be times when you have no choice at all but, where possible, you should consider such factors as wind direction and possible access routes and the cover they provide for yourself, as well as the position of the normal routes taken by the animals. The hide itself may have to be camouflaged with vegetation for, while this will make no difference to the animals, it may prevent its attracting the attention of curious humans. Humans are the one animal you do not want to attract, their interference may scare the animals away altogether and it often results in damage to the hide.

The sudden appearance of an artificial contrivance is often quite sufficient to cause many animals to desert the area, and so they should be introduced to the hide slowly. The first method of achieving this is to erect the hide some distance away and then, over the period of days, move it closer and closer until it is in the desired position. The second method is more suitable for restricted situations such as small clearings in woodland – the hide is erected in place over a period of days. The poles of the frame can be left on the ground first of all, next the frame is erected, then the cover put nearby. Later the cover is half put on the frame, being certain that all loose fabric is secured to prevent flapping, and eventually the whole structure is completed and in place. The time taken in moving the hide into position or from frame to the complete structure will vary with the locality and the animals concerned. If they show any signs of distress at all the process should be ceased, the hide dismantled and the creatures left alone. Another, slower, approach can be attempted after a few days' absence. Some animals will not tolerate disturbance of any sort and these should be left alone immediately. The welfare of the

Fig 43   The 'high seat' is especially useful when looking at deer

animals is your first concern and you should always play safe
and, if anything, be over cautious. During the period of 'hide
acclimatisation' you should make detailed notes regarding
your method of approach and the reactions to it. Whilst no
two animals, even of the same species, will react in the same
way, you will at least have guidelines from which to work in
the future.

The 'High Seat'
There are times when even a hide at ground level, no matter
how well positioned or camouflaged, will not meet with the
approval of the animals being watched. It is then that what
naturalists know as a 'high seat' can be so useful. The high seat
can be as simple as a ladder propped against a tree, or it can be
a static, free-standing, raised hide. Whichever type you use,
you will find that it is well worth it as it immediately takes
you out of the normal line of sight and smell of the animals
you want to watch. High seats are especially useful for deer
watching but many other animals can be viewed to advantage
from such a vantage point; some of my best views of Foxes have
been gained while I was up in the air.

12 PHOTOGRAPHY AND RADIO TRACKING

Photography

Photographing wildlife in its natural surroundings, whether for a clear record shot or as an art form, is one of the most demanding as well as one of the most rewarding aspects of field natural history. Nocturnal wildlife photography is almost a science in itself and, because it is still in the early stages of development, there is plenty of scope for innovation from the amateur prepared to master the combination of skills which working at night when light conditions are low demands, and which can only be improved with practice. Recent advances in camera and electronic technology have produced a plethora of equipment which make the task considerably easier than that of the pioneers of nature photography of fifty years ago. Some of this equipment is quite expensive, but even with relatively modest camera and flash very good results can be obtained.

Spotlights and Electronic Flash

Using available, or natural, light at night is virtually out of the question for most purposes. The low light levels and consequently the long exposure times required are not sufficient to make a good photograph unless you are trying to capture an organism which emits its own light in the form of bioluminescence – some fungi and Glow-worms for instance. An artificial light source will normally be required and the type you use will depend on the subject of the photograph.

Static objects such as plants and many invertebrates lend themselves to steady illumination from spotlights which usually require some time to set up and to measure the correct light level. Even vertebrates such as Badgers, Foxes, some small mammals and some birds will stay still long enough or be so indifferent to bright lights to make spotlights usable. However, individuals even within the same species vary in their reaction, and if any distress is shown by the subject the project should be abandoned. The use of spotlights, however, is helpful when making cine films of nocturnal animals, in fact without the more sophisticated equipment of infra-red lighting (see page 196) it is the only way to obtain pictures. At first a red-filtered light source should be used, followed by a combination of red and white light. Gradually over a period of time, normally dictated by the animals themselves, the white light is increased in intensity until you have the required level to make filming possible. A similar technique can be used for still photography, but in many cases is unnecessary; electronic flash is much easier, the equipment being cheaper and far less bulky.

Electronic flash is by far the most convenient source of light for nocturnal photography. Small powerful units, either attached to the camera by the hot shoe or on leads, are fired at the same time as the shutter is released and provide a brilliant flash to illuminate the subject. Very simple units powered by normal dry batteries can be purchased for a few pounds – such flash heads are semi-automatic in their operation and the camera settings for shutter speed and aperture are calculated from a scale on the flash unit itself. Flash units with rechargeable batteries, either wet-cell or nickel-cadmium cell, are also available, and have the advantage that they can be fully charged before you go out for the night, thus lessening the risk of running out of power at the critical moment. More sophisticated 'computer' flash heads actually work out the correct exposure for the film being used and turn themselves off after the requisite amount of light has been delivered. When used in conjunction with some of the modern electronically controlled cameras, the equipment virtually takes the picture by itself.

The intense light caused by a flash discharge does not normally bother animals too much, but it may cause temporary blindness which, in flying birds, can result in collisions. Where flash is to be used regularly at one site, for example a Badger sett, it is a good idea to accustom the animals to the idea first before actually attempting to take any pictures. Some sort of reflector positioned near the site will normally suffice – a favourite trick of bird watchers is to place tin lids on the outside of the hides. Only on deer, perhaps, does the use of any kind of reflector have the opposite of the desired effect; indeed reflectors are used along roads as a means of scaring deer away.

Auto-winders and Automatic Firing Devices

Auto-winders can be purchased to fit many cameras, and in the correct circumstances make nocturnal photography very much easier. Essentially these devices move on the frames of film automatically and, while doing so, release the shutter and fire the flash units if they are attached. At least two, and up to five, frames per second can be achieved by the use of auto-wind, depending on the make of camera and the amount of money spent, but do make sure that the recycling time of the flash unit can keep pace with the speed of the winder, otherwise you will fire off film which is not exposed. Bulk film holders can be used in association with many types of auto-winder giving the distinct advantage that rolls of film do not have to be changed so often, minimising the risk of disturbing the subject. Another source of disturbance is the noise of the auto-wind mechanism itself, and the sound-insulation covers which will cut this to a low level and which can be fitted to many cameras are particularly useful in this connection.

The great advantage of auto-winders in nature photography is that in conjunction with various control mechanisms which can be operated from a distance, camera and photographer need not be together when the picture is taken. Having set up the camera with the correct focusing, shutter speed etc, the photographer retires to a reasonable distance from which he can survey the scene with a red-filtered torch and await the moment of exposure. Many devices are available for manually

Fig 44 The combination of a long cable release and a motor drive on your camera will enable you to observe your subjects from a distance and thus conceal your presence

releasing camera shutters by remote control, one of the simplest being the air-pressure bulb – a long plastic tube fitted with a bulb which, when squeezed by the photographer, moves a plunger fitted to the shutter-release button which in turn activates the camera. Most auto-winders, however, are electrically operated by a simple switching device on the end of a long cable, rather like a slide-projector control cable.

Obviously when using such manual devices you will need to be constantly alert to catch the animal on film at the correct moment, and this can be very tiring. Some animals will not tolerate your presence even at a distance, or there may be no suitable vantage point from which to watch. In such circumstances one of the many automatic firing devices whereby you can walk away and let the animal and the camera between them take the picture can prove useful. One of the most effective, and thus the one most used by professionals is where the camera is activated by a beam of light broken by the animal. Ordinary light aimed at a photocell, or infra-red light used with a detector, are the two methods normally used, the beam being aligned so that it crosses the expected path of the animal. The only problem is that, with one beam of light, focusing can be difficult as the animal is able to break the beam anywhere along its length. Alignment of the camera along the beam, and camera adjustments to give the maximum depth of field, go some way to overcoming this, but an easier way is to use two beams of light. The detectors for these two beams are wired up so that they will only fire when both beams are broken at the same instant and, if the actual beams are arranged so that they cross each other, there will only be one point at which this can happen – the point on which you have already focused your camera. The use of more than two beams opens up all sorts of possibilities and refinements. If a number of beams is rigged so that they have to be broken in sequence before the camera is activated, you can dictate the direction of approach of the animal which will allow the picture to be taken. Thus you can make the camera only take pictures of what you require, though this depends very much on the animal deciding to approach the way you want it to, and the camera may remain set up all night without a picture being taken.

Automatic triggering devices are produced for use with many makes of camera, but anyone with some skill in electronics could easily make his own. For the less sophisticated, semi-mechanical devices can be used. Various tilting platforms which activate switches when the animal steps on them should be within the expertise of most people.

Open-shutter Photography

Open-shutter photography is a method worth trying by those who do not have access to more sophisticated equipment. Essentially, the camera is focused and otherwise set but the shutter is left open; and attached to the camera are flash units which, by some means such as the slave units mentioned below, are fired at the correct moment to take the picture of the animal. Light levels should be very low otherwise a ghost image will appear on the negative due to natural light; this sort of photography is therefore only effective on the darkest nights. The major disadvantage is that only one picture can be taken at a time, and you then have to approach the camera to wind on the film for the next shot.

Although open-shutter photography is a simple technique in itself it can be linked with stroboscopic flash to produce exciting photographs. Strobe flash units emit a series of individual light pulses – about fifty per second is a useful number – and this has the effect of stopping the action of moving animals such as bats or birds in flight; thus a number of exposures of the same subject taken within one second can be obtained on the same negative. Such effects have been of great help in untangling the complexities of animal locomotion, but this equipment can be expensive and is normally used in conjunction with the light-beam detectors already described.

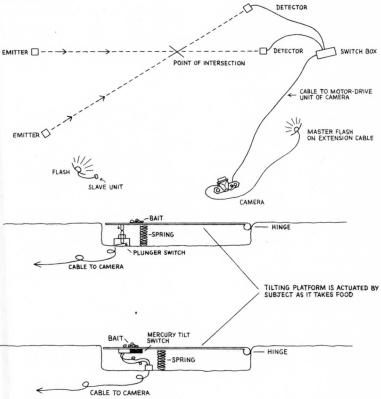

Fig 45   Crossed infra-red beams (above) or tilting platforms with switches (below) are ways of ensuring that your camera will fire at the correct time and in the correct place even when you might be miles away

Slave Units

Most nocturnal photography requires the use of two flash units in order to eliminate the harsh shadows which result from using only one; but it is important that synchronisation is achieved. If the units are close together they can be linked to each other and to the camera by a Y-junction. For greater distances an electronic slave unit is desirable. Slave units are photosensitive switches which are attached to the flash head and are triggered by the light from a second flash head, the difference between the two pulses is so small as to be negligible and thus will not affect the results. Slave units can also be used with open-shutter photography as a means of firing the on-site flash units. The photographer should stand well behind the camera and at the right moment a third hand-held flash is activated which trips the slave unit and thus fires the flashes.

Image Intensifiers

Image intensification is a process by which available light reflected from an object is collected and amplified electronically in order to produce an image on a small television screen. It is particularly useful at very low light intensities and as such would seem to be an ideal tool for nocturnal observations; indeed it was developed for this very purpose, but with military rather than natural targets in mind. Image intensifiers have been much used recently in the production of wildlife films, but as they are expensive they are beyond the scope of most naturalists.

Infra-red Light

Infra-red light is another technique for observing animals in low light conditions. It is invisible to the animals and as such enables them to maintain more natural behaviour than would otherwise be possible. However, it is also beyond our range of perception, and a converter must be used for us to see the object of scrutiny. Infra-red light is most useful when taking ciné film of animals at night, but still photography can also be enhanced by its use as the subject can be kept in view all the time, thus making it easier to take your picture at the correct moment. Special film sensitive to infra-red light will, however, have to be used, and the camera will have to be carefully set. The improvement over a red torch and flash is debatable, and for most work the added expense will probably be unjustified.

Setting Up

When setting up the camera and associated equipment, make sure it isn't in any danger from mishap. If large mammals such as Badger or Fox are being photographed, the camera – normally on a sturdy tripod – will need to be firmly lashed to some support to prevent its being knocked over by the subject. And remember that your equipment should be bought with its showerproof quality in mind. This is particularly important with high-voltage electronic flash which can be dangerous in damp conditions.

Sound-insulation covers, already mentioned in connection with auto-winders, are, in fact, recommended for any nocturnal wildlife photography.

Radio Tracking

Radio tracking and radioactive marking are modern methods of following animals from a distance. For the first-named, larger mammals are fitted with a small radio transmitter and then released, after which a receiver fitted with direction finders pinpoints the animals whereabouts. The small transmitter does not significantly affect the animal's way of life and so interesting aspects of behaviour, diurnal rhythms and territoriality can be observed in as near natural conditions as possible.

Radio-isotope marking is a recognised technique used in many fields of biology, but as far as nocturnal wildlife is concerned its most important application is in the tracking of small mammals. The radio-active substances used are not harmful, and are generally attached as a small ring to the animal's leg. The animal is then released at the point of capture and followed with a Geiger counter. Much has been learned in this way, particularly about voles and Moles.

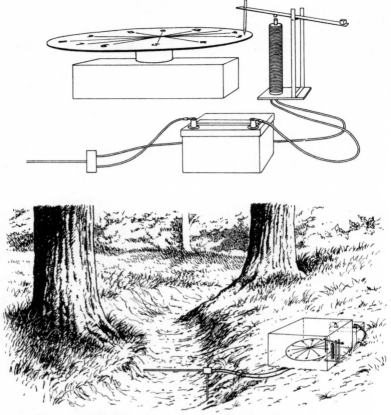

Fig 46 A simple timer placed across an animal's run can tell much about the movements and emergent times of the creature you wish to study

Both these methods are extremely specialised, and both require licences; as such they are beyond the scope of most amateurs.

Automatic Timers

Automatic timing devices can be used to register exactly when an animal has passed a particular place and thus greatly reduce the frustration of waiting. Simply by leaving a timing device in the expected path of an animal or at the entrance to its lair, you will gain valuable information about its comings and goings and times of emergence.

With the advent of micro electronics, there are now switches and computer-controlled timing devices on the market. All that is needed is some form of clock, a switch to register the animal's passing and a means of marking the actual time. A simple timer can be made from an old central-heating timer clock and a felt-tip pen. A disc is attached to the clock so that it completes a revolution every twelve hours. The pen is attached to a solenoid (electro-magnet) and some form of switch to activate the mechanism is necessary. This may be a pressure pad (see Fig 45), or a twig placed across the expected path of the animal. A further sophistication is to attach the switch to an automatic camera so that when an animal passes, it takes its own photograph as well as that of the clock. There can then be no doubt as to what is passing a particular place at a particular time.

APPENDIX:
SCIENTIFIC NAMES OF ANIMALS IN THE TEXT

Adder	*Vipera berus*
Avocet	*Recurvirostra avosetta*
Badger	*Meles meles*
Bat, Brown Long-eared	*Plecotus auritus*
Bat, Daubenton's	*Myotis daubentoni*
Bat, Greater Horseshoe	*Rhinolophus ferrumequinum*
Bat, Grey Long-eared	*Plecotus austriacus*
Bat, Lesser Horseshoe	*Rhinolophus hipposideros*
Bat, Noctule	*Nyctalus noctula*
Bat, Pipistrelle	*Pipistrellus pipistrellus*
Bat, Serotine	*Eptesicus serotinus*
Beetle, Elm Bark	*Scolytus scolytus*
Beetle, Lesser Stag	*Dorcus parallelopipedus*
Beetle, Stag	*Lucanus cervus*
Beetle, Wasp	*Clytus arietus*
Bittern	*Botaurus stellaris*
Brandling	*Eisenia foetida*
Bush-cricket, Dark	*Pholidoptera griseoaptera*
Bush-cricket, Great Green	*Tettigonia viridissima*
Bush-cricket, Oak	*Meconema thalassinum*
Cat, Domestic	*Felis domesticus*
Cat, Wild	*Felis sylvestris*
Coach Horse, Devil's	*Ocypus olens*
Cockchafer	*Melolontha melolontha*
Cockroach, American	*Periplaneta americana*
Cockroach, Common	*Blatta orientalis*
Cockroach, Dusky	*Ectobius lapponicus*
Cockroach, German	*Blatella germanica*
Cockroach, Lesser	*Ectobius panzeri*
Cockroach, Tawny	*Ectobius pallidus*

Coot	*Fulica atra*
Corncrake	*Crex crex*
Cricket, House	*Acheta domestica*
Curlew	*Numenius arquata*
Deer, Fallow	*Dama dama*
Deer, Red	*Cervus elephas*
Deer, Roe	*Capreolus capreolus*
Duck, Tufted	*Aythya fuligula*
Earthworm, Common	*Lumbricus terrestris*
Earwig	*Labia minor*
Eggar, Oak	*Lasiocampa quercus*
Ferret	*Mustela furo*
Fieldmouse, Long-tailed	*see Woodmouse*
Fieldmouse, Yellow-necked	*Apodemus flavicollis*
Firebrat	*Thermobia domestica*
Fox	*Vulpes vulpes*
Frog, Common	*Rana temporaria*
Glow-worm	*Lampyris noctiluca*
Godwit, Bar-tailed	*Limosa lapponica*
Godwit, Black-tailed	*-Limosa limosa*
Goose, Bean	*Anser fabialis*
Goose, Brent	*Branta bernicula*
Goose, Pink-footed	*Anser brachyrhynchus*
Hare, Brown	*Lepus capensis*
Hare, Mountain	*Lepus timidus*
Hawkmoth, Bedstraw	*Hyles galii*
Hawkmoth, Death's Head	*Acherontia atropos*
Hawkmoth, Elephant	*Deilephila elpenor*
Hawkmoth, Privet	*Sphinx ligustri*
Hedgehog	*Erinaceus europaeus*
Heron, Grey	*Ardea cinerea*
Heron, Night	*Nycticorax nycticorax*
Knot	*Calidris canutus*
Mallard	*Anas platyrhynchos*
Marten, Pine	*Martes martes*
Mink, American	*Mustela vison*
Mole	*Talpa europaea*
Mole-cricket	*Gryllotalpa gryllotalpa*
Moorhen	*Gallinula chloropus*

Moth, Emperor	*Saturnia pavonia*
Moth, Large White Plume	*Pterophorus pentadactyla*
Moth, Swallow-tailed	*Ourapterix sambucaria*
Moth, Winter	*Operophtera brumata*
Mouse, Harvest	*Micromys minutus*
Mouse, House	*Mus musculus*
Newt, Great-crested	*Triturus cristatus*
Newt, Palmate	*Triturus helveticus*
Newt, Smooth	*Triturus vulgaris*
Nightingale	*Luscinia megarhynchos*
Nightjar	*Caprimulgus europaeus*
Otter	*Lutra lutra*
Owl, Barn	*Tyto alba*
Owl, Little	*Athene noctua*
Owl, Long-eared	*Asio otus*
Owl, Short-eared	*Asio flammeus*
Owl, Snowy	*Nyctea scandiaca*
Owl, Tawny	*Strix aluco*
Oystercatcher	*Haematopus ostralegus*
Polecat	*Mustela putorius*
Rabbit	*Oryctolagus cuniculus*
Rail, Water	*Rallus aquaticus*
Rat, Black	*Rattus rattus*
Rat, Brown	*Rattus norvegicus*
Robin	*Erithacus rubecula*
Shrew, Common	*Sorex araneus*
Shrew, Pygmy	*Sorex minutus*
Shrew, Water	*Neomys fodiens*
Silverfish	*Lepisma saccharina*
Slow-worm	*Anguis fragilis*
Slug, Garden	*Arion hortensis*
Slug, Great Grey	*Limax maximus*
Snipe	*Gallinago gallinago*
Spider, 'Daddy Long-legs'	*Pholcus phalangioides*
Spider, Garden	*Araneus diadematus*
Spider, Water	*Argyroneta aquatica*
Starling	*Sturnus vulgaris*
Stoat	*Mustela erminea*
Swan, Mute	*Cygnus olor*

Teal	*Anas crecca*
Toad, Common	*Bufo bufo*
Toad, Natterjack	*Bufo calamita*
Turnstone	*Arenaria interpres*
Underwing, Red	*Catocala nupta*
Vole, Bank	*Clethrionomys glareolus*
Vole, Common	*Microtus arvalis*
Vole, Field	*Microtus agrestis*
Vole, Guernsey	*Microtus arvalis sarnius*
Vole, Orkney	*Microtus arvalis orcadensis*
Vole, Water	*Arvicola terrestris*
Wagtail, Pied	*Motacilla alba*
Warbler, Cetti's	*Cettia cetti*
Warbler, Grasshopper	*Locustella naevia*
Warbler, Reed	*Acrocephalus scirpaceus*
Warbler, Sedge	*Acrocephalus schoenobaenus*
Wartbiter	*Decticus verrucivorus*
Weasel	*Mustela nivalis*
Wigeon	*Anas penelope*
Woodcock	*Scolopax rusticola*
Woodmouse	*Apodemus sylvaticus*

FURTHER READING

Inevitably with a book such as this, which has a broad scope and has been preceded by over one hundred years of study, the literature is voluminous and to detail every article or publication would be an impossible task. I have, therefore, had to be selective, so that the following references are those which have been most useful to me or are in themselves a good introduction to the study of nocturnal animals. To the many authors not mentioned but consulted, I express my gratitude. I could not have written this book without their hard work.

Andrzeweski, R. and Olszewski, J. 'Social behaviour and inter-specific relations in *Apodemus flavicollis* and *Clethrionomys glareolus*', Acta Theriologica (1963), 155–68

Beames, I. 'The spread of the Fox in the London area', Ecologist, 2 no 2 (1972), 25–6

Bevan, G. 'The food of Tawny Owls in London', *London Bird Report*, 29 (1964), 56–72

Brown, L. E. 'Field experiments on the activity of the small mammals, *Apodemus, Clethrionomys,* and *Microtus*' Proceedings Zoological Society of London, 126 (1956), 549–64

Brown, L. H. and Lasiewski, R. C. 'Metabolism of Weasels; The cost of being long and thin', Ecology, 53 (1972), 939–43

Burrows, R. *Wild Fox*, David & Charles (1968)

Burton, R. *Animal Senses*, David & Charles (1973)

Butterfield, J. (et al) 'Studies on the distribution, food, breeding biology and relative abundance of the Pygmy and Common Shrews (*Sorex minutus* and *S. araneus*) in upland areas of northern England', *Journal Zoological Society of London*, 195 no 2 (1981), 169–80

Chapman, R. F. and Sankey, J. H. P. 'The larger invertebrate fauna of three rabbit carcasses', *Journal of Animal Ecology* 24 (1955), 395–402

Chitty, D. and Kempson, D. A. 'Prebaiting small mammals and a new design of live trap', *Ecology*, 30 (1949), 536–42

Chitty, D. and Shorten, M. 'Techniques for the study of the Norway

Rat (*Rattus norvegicus*)', *Journal of Mammalogy*, 27 (1946), 63–78

Corbet, G. B. and Southern, H. N. eds. *The Handbook of British Mammals*, Mammal Society; Blackwell Scientific (1977)

Crowcroft, P. 'The daily cycle of activity in British Shrews', *Proceedings Zoological Society of London*, 123 (1954), 715–29

Crowcroft, P. *The Life of the Shrew*, Reinhardt (1957)

Eason, E. H. *Centipedes of the British Isles*, Warne (1964)

Edwards, C. A. and Lofty, J. R. *The Biology of Earthworms*, Chapman & Hall (1972)

Finley, R. B. Jnr. 'Observations of Nocturnal Animals by Red Light', *Journal of Mammalogy*, 40 no 4 (1959), 591–4

Glue, D. E. 'Avian Predator pellet analysis and the mammalogist', *Mammal Review*, 1 (1970), 53–61

Glue, D. E. 'Food of the Barn Owl in Britain and Ireland', *Bird Study*, 21 (1974), 200–10

Gould, E., Nevus, N. C. and Novick, A. 'Evidence for echolocation in shrews', *Journal of Experimental Zoology*, 156 (1964), 19–38

Griffin, D. R. *Listening in the Dark*, Yale University Press (1958)

Harris, S. *Secret Life of the Harvest Mouse*, Hamlyn (1979)

Hibbert-Ware, A. 'Report of the Little Owl Food Enquiry, 1937–8', *British Birds*, 31 (1937–8), 162–87, 205–29, 249–64

Hoffmeyer, I. and Sales, G. P. 'Ultrasonic behaviour of *Apodemus sylvaticus* and *A. flavicollis*', *Oikos*, 29 (1977), 67–77

Hooper, J. H. D. 'Potential use of a portable ultrasonic receiver for the field identification of flying bats', *Ultrasonics*, 7 (1969), 177–81

Jacobson, M. and Beroza, M. 'Insect Attractants', *Scientific American*, 211 no 2 (1964), 20–7

Lenton, E. 'Otters and the Otter Haven Project', *Nature In Devon*, 3 (1982), 27–43

Lloyd, H. G. 'Habitat requirements of the Red Fox', in Zimen, E. 'The Red Fox', *Biogeographica*, 18 (1981)

Lloyd, J. R. 'Factors affecting the emergence times of the Badger (*Meles meles*) in Britain', *Journal Zoological Society of London*, 155 (1968), 223–32

MacDonald, D. W. 'Nocturnal Observations of Tawny Owls (*Strix aluco*) preying upon earthworms', *Ibis*, 118 (1976), 579–80

Mellanby, K. *The Mole*, New Naturalist Monographs, Collins (1971)

Montgomery, W. I. 'The use of arboreal runways by the woodland rodents, *Apodemus sylvaticus, A. flavicollis* and *Clethrionomys glareolus*', *Mammal Review*, 10 no 4 (1980), 189–95

Neal, E. *Badgers*, Blandford (1977)

Payne, R. S. 'How the Barn Owl locates prey by hearing', *The Living Bird*, 1 (1962), 151–9

Richards, O. W. and Davies, R. G. *Imm's General Textbook of Entomology*, Chapman & Hall (1977)

Roeder, K. D. 'Moths and Ultrasound', *Scientific American*, 212 no 4 (1965), 94–102

Roots, C. *Animals of the Dark*, David & Charles (1974)

South, G. R. 'Food of the Long-eared Owl in South Lancashire', *British Birds*, Vol 59 (1966), 493–7

Southern, H. N. et al 'Watching nocturnal animals by infra-red radiation', *Journal of Animal Ecology*, 15 (1946), 198–202

Southern, H. N. et al 'Tawny owls and their prey', 96 (1954), 384–410

Sparks, J. and Soper, A. *Owls: Their natural and unnatural history*, David & Charles (1975)

Tansley, K. *Vision in Vertebrates*, Chapman & Hall (1965)

Thompson, H. V. and Worden, A. N. *The Rabbit*, New Naturalist Monographs; Collins (1956)

Vesey-Fitzgerald, B. *British Bats*, Methuen (1949)

Vesey-Fitzgerald, B. *Town Fox, Country Fox*, Country Book Club (1968)

Vickery, W. L. and Bider, J. R. 'The influence of weather on rodent activity', *Journal of Mammalogy*, 62 no 1 (1981), 140–5

Village, A. 'The Diet and Breeding of Long-eared Owls in Relation to Vole Numbers', *Bird Study*, 28 (1981), 215–24

Watmough, B. R. 'Observations on nocturnal feeding by Night Herons, *Nycticorax nycticorax*, Ibis 120 (1968), 356–8

Williams, C. B. 'The influence of moonlight on the activity of certain nocturnal insects, particularly of the family Noctuidae as indicated by a light trap', *Philosophical Transactions Royal Society of London* (B), 226 (1936), 357–80

Witherby, et al *The Handbook of British Birds*, H. F. and G. Witherby (1941)

Yalden, B. W. and Morris, P. A. *The Lives of Bats*, David & Charles (1975)

INDEX